BASIC
ENGINEERING MECHANICS
Explained

The foundation of engineering knowledge

Gregory Pastoll, PhD (Higher Ed) BSc Mech Eng

Copyright and Origination

The contents of this work are entirely the work of this author, who retains the copyright in them.

Besides a few historical images that are in the public domain, all the illustrations are the work of the author.

This work was first published by Gregory Pastoll, in 2019

Cover design by Ross MacLennan

Cover artwork by Gregory Pastoll

ISBN   978-0-6484665-0-5 (hardcover)

ISBN   978-0-6484665-1-2 (paperback)

ISBN   978-0-6484665-6-7 (e-book)

Preface

I have written this book because, as someone who has taught engineering mechanics enthusiastically for over 14 years, I believe that mechanics is interesting, easy and relevant to many aspects of our daily life.

None of the books on mechanics that I have seen give that impression, so this book is an attempt to redress that issue. I have tried here to present the material in a way that makes the content self-evidently useful and appealing.

As a young lecturer in basic mechanical engineering subjects at the former Cape Technikon, in Cape Town, South Africa, I experimented with teaching methods, and began to develop an understanding of what was needed to give students a practical 'handle' on what they were learning.

While teaching there, I was greatly inspired by the successes achieved by John Cowan, a visiting lecturer, in making university learning in the field of engineering truly 'hands-on'. At the time, Cowan was a lecturer in civil engineering at Heriot-Watt University in Scotland. He later went on to become Professor of Learning Development at The Open University of the UK. After attending his talk in Cape Town, I read some of his publications, and later visited his unit. I could see in the way he taught, that it was possible for students to learn about principles and techniques by taking responsibility for their own learning. Cowan's dedication to this ideal inspired me to explore what was really important in my teaching, and to keep on developing better ways of teaching.

Subsequent to my first 5-year spell of lecturing basic engineering subjects, for a further 14 years I was a consultant in teaching methods at the University of Cape Town. There I was directly exposed to the teaching methods in use in all the different Faculties of the University, and learnt a great deal from trying to work with my colleagues towards ways of improving their own teaching.

This knowledge I summarised in a book entitled 'Motivating People to Learn', and I put what I learnt there to good use when I again went into teaching engineering mechanics, for a second spell of 9 years.

The present book is intended to give the the reader the opportunity to:

- Remain interested in and motivated by the subject,

- See how these principles can be applied to a wide range of practical situations,

- Learn to reason out solutions to new problems from first principles, and

- Develop a perspective on the limitations of determining answers by calculations.

The topics covered in the book do not necessarily follow any particular prescribed curriculum. The book contains the essential topics in mechanics found in most curricula, simply because those topics undeniably form the basis of the science of mechanics.

I have added what I perceive to be context-enriching material, about certain historical aspects of the science of mechanics. Rather than keep the content to a minimum, I have opted to include everything I can think of that might broaden a reader's understanding. This has made it necessary to spread the book over three volumes.

Acknowledgements

Professor John Cowan for his many hours spent in patient perusal of my developing chapters and giving me excellent feedback.

Mark Kilfoil for occasional checking and verifying of approaches and calculations.

My mother, Lois, for believing in me since I was born. My late father, Gerald, for showing his children by example always to question everything and to think things through for themselves.

Nick Hampton for telling me that I make it look simpler than it really is, which amused me greatly, as I believe that such a view comes from other authors having created the impression that mechanics is more complicated than it really is.

Those of my ex-colleagues who, over the years, bemusedly, but loyally and voluntarily, assisted me in the often wearisome task of adjudicating some of the design-and-build projects that I assigned to my students. There are too many who helped in some way for me to recall everyone. However, particular support came from Joseph Basakayi, Ian Noble-Jack, John Byett, Margot Lynn, Dave Evans, Eric Obeng and Mark Ludick.

The late Hugh Williams, a brilliant technician who built many unique pieces of laboratory apparatus for me in my first spell of teaching. A most respected, competent and inspiring gentleman, whose input to my laboratory classes was invaluable.

The support and understanding shown me by my wife Lindsay during the long process of getting the book written and illustrated. Without her, I could not have got this far.

This book is dedicated to the thousands of students who have passed through my classes. Thank you for being there so I could try to work out how better to guide your learning. I hope you had fun, and that you retain good memories of your engagement with mechanics. I do.

Gregory Pastoll

Foreword

by John Cowan, Emeritus Professor of Learning Development, UK Open University

This set of three volumes is the work of an enthusiast. Greg has long approached the subject, the teaching and the facilitation of students' learning of applied mechanics, with an inherent enthusiasm which he generously and infectively shares with his readers. With a keen awareness that learners in this subject area must go beyond *understanding* the concepts and theory to *applying* them, he follows his initial instruction by offering a generous provision of examples. With an experienced teacher's wisdom, he appreciates that such a series could prove wearisome or off-putting for both over-confident or uncertain learners. He thus presents many of his almost standard examples wrapped up for variety in motivating and brief scenario settings.

Motivation and interest have been high on his list of priorities as a writer; so, too, has been the fundamental task of explaining principles, concepts and methods. He covers this comprehensively, competently and in a logical and well-explained sequence. This series has been constructed with meticulous attention paid to the needs of the learners who are the readers. Reader-friendly language is used throughout. New terms are introduced timeously and clearly, but never in the tedious and formal detail which can bedevil many texts on this subject.

Occasionally Greg indulges in the familiar eccentricity of the born teacher by wandering off into a digression in which he tells an interesting "wee story". He airs relevant comments and recounts interesting historical accounts or anecdotes, whose mastery may not be necessary in grasping the fundamental principles and approaches, but whose value in retaining the interest of the reader while enhancing their relevant knowledge is noteworthy.

From time to time, his writing includes wry comments which brought a smile to the lips of this reader. This contributes subtly to his writer's efforts to establish a relationship with his readers in which he and they engage together in the learning and teaching of applied mechanics. The text is also enriched by the inclusion of many attractive and relevant sketches from Greg's able hand, through which he contributes further to the personal nature of the teacher/student relationship housed in these pages.

The series has been conceived on the basis of extensive and reflectively reviewed teaching in this area coupled with wide reading of the approaches followed by others. For Greg has been enthusiastically seeking to address the assorted needs of learners of varied ability, experience and motivation.

The result is comprehensive and developmental coverage of the principles and practice of applied mechanics. In my judgement, the end result is almost self-sufficient for any learner who wishes to master this subject area by following this text which lends itself to use in the context which has been called the "flipped classroom".

Here study time begins with time spent assimilating a provided teaching input on text or video. This is then followed by class time in which the teacher, supported by peers, addresses difficulties and questions, and then facilitates the addressing of tasks designed to deepen the learning and consolidate the understanding. This text would be a wonderful source for self-managed learning time, and many of its activities ideal for the follow-up time.

I am somewhat sad that, with my advancing years, the opportunity to build in this way on Greg's work is not open to me; but it is open for today's teachers and today's learners, whom I collegially urge to take advantage of it.

John Cowan

Contents outline for the series

Volume 1: Principles and static forces

Volume 2: Motion and energy

Volume 3: Rotation and inertia

Contents: Volume 1

Principles and static forces

Chapter 1

What Mechanics is about and why we study it

- *What the science of mechanics includes.*
- *How our present knowledge of mechanics evolved.*
- *How the science of mechanics fits into engineering.*
- *Is there much to learn in order to master basic mechanics?*
- *In which fields of engineering is a knowledge of mechanics essential?*
- *Why mechanics remains an essential field of science.*

What the science of Mechanics includes

The science of mechanics deals with anything that helps us understand the interactions between objects in the physical world. It deals with the behaviour of solids, liquids, and gases when acted on by forces. It deals with the rules that govern the equilibrium and movement of objects, and with the ways that energy is transferred.

This knowledge is essential to engineers, because they need to understand how the physical world behaves in order to design products and processes that work.

Any item we build will inevitably conform with the laws of nature. If we know what those laws are, we can make sure to account for most of the variables that affect our designs. If we overlook any of the likely consequences of what we propose to build, disaster may result.

An example of applying the known laws of nature to designing an entirely new device that worked:

The airship in which Henri Giffard of France flew a distance of 15 miles, in 1852. His craft was powered by a 3 HP steam engine, and averaged a speed of 6 miles per hour.

How our present-day knowledge of mechanics has evolved

Most of what any given person knows about mechanics is the result of practical observations we have made in our own lives. You see how material objects and forces interact in nature, and you store this understanding somewhere in your subconscious.

It is common knowledge that the wind can push, stones are heavy, water spills. You don't need mathematics or diagrams to understand that these effects occur, or to propose how to put them to use.

Even at a very young age, it didn't take you long to find out what made your side of the see-saw descend. You didn't have to be told 'the rules'.

Every child that has played with a ball, built dams of mud or used a stick to lever a rock out of a hole, has started to build up an intuitive appreciation of the principles of mechanics.

By learning about some of the mathematical relationships that apply to the laws of mechanics, we can obtain some handy short cuts for solving certain types of problem. However, if we don't know anything about mechanics *intuitively*, from our own experience, we could stare at the maths as long as we like, but it wouldn't make sense.

Looking back in time, there was an era when a formalised knowledge of mechanics was almost certainly *not* employed to aid in design. People made extensive use of mechanical principles that were discovered through experience. They developed weapons for hunting, implements for farming and tools for accomplishing their daily domestic tasks.

This era occupied almost all of human history. Anyone who needed to make objects did so using wood, stone, plant fibres, leather and clay, and learnt their trades by practical experience, not by book learning.

The boomerang, for example, has sophisticated aerodynamics, and is a prime example of a functional device developed by trial and error, without the use of written language or mathematics.

Another example of a design with great sophistication, developed almost certainly by trial and error, and without the use of mathematics or formalised principles of mechanics, is that of the war chariots used by the Egyptians.

In many cultures around the world, ingenuity and common sense were behind the development of machines and processes that fulfilled a function in daily life, not only in war.

Among the artefacts built on the basis of trial and error, and small refinements to traditional designs, were lathes, rope-twisting machines, bellows, farming machinery, shipping vessels, water wheels, pumps and wheeled vehicles of every description.

Most of human history has taken place in a purely mechanical age, in which every machine and process was entirely mechanical, powered by human or animal energy, or that supplied by wind and water. This period lasted until about 300 years ago, when steam power was introduced, to be followed by other power sources and technologies.

We can trace the beginnings of the science of mechanics to the ancient Greeks, who produced brilliant thinkers like Archimedes, Euclid, Aristotle, Archytas and Pythagoras. These were people who were intrigued by how nature works, who tried to find some orderly way of describing the principles that seemed to govern the interactions of physical objects. They did this not just for the sake of science, but with a view to practical applications.

A Greek warship. The Greeks made significant advances in a variety of technologies: in war machines, in metalwork and in building construction with stone.

3

Until the 1700s, people hadn't divided up science into branches, as we do today. The man of science (invariably men, in those days) turned his talents to everything he noticed, not only to mechanical phenomena. Such men were not called 'scientists', but 'natural philosophers': people who thought about and tried to explain all the ways in which nature behaves, and who, much like we do, tried to turn this knowledge to useful account.

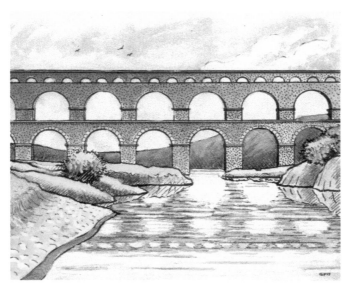

The aqueduct, at Nîmes, France, as it stands today.

People in the ancient world built some very clever machines and structures, despite the fact that they did not possess the mathematics or the technologies that we have today. The artefacts they built were not necessarily crude, either.

An excellent example of the precision commanded by historical engineers can be found in the construction of the Roman aqueducts, which were gravity-powered water channels, built to conduct water from mountain springs to cities.

When building an aqueduct, it was (and still is) very important to construct the channel with the correct gradient. If a channel is too steep, the water will race downhill, building up enough speed to cause a problem at the output end.

Also, eventually the passage of fast-flowing water will erode the relatively soft limestone of the channel itself. On the other hand, if a channel is not steep enough, the water won't flow at all.

This particular aqueduct was built to convey water through hilly country, for a distance of 51 km, with twists and turns, over bridges built across ravines, with a total drop, from water source to delivery point, of only 17 metres. [1] This amounts to a drop of only 1 metre in every 3 km or a gradient of approximately 1 in 3000. The majority of Roman aqueducts were built with even finer gradients, sometimes up to 1 in 8000. To accomplish that degree of accuracy with modern surveying equipment would be a feat to be proud of. To do it without such equipment is particularly impressive.

In the thousand years after the Romans, mechanics continued to be applied in a primarily intuitive way. It is difficult to determine when or how some some formalised principles were recognised as useful in machine design. A device was simply built: if it worked, who cared what the mathematical principles were that described why it worked?

To reinforce the lack of seeming need for theory, we have only to look at the drawings of Leonardo da Vinci (1452 -1519), the Renaissance genius who left us hundreds of designs for intriguing mechanical contraptions. Leonardo himself admitted a lack of theoretical training, but that did not stop him from applying his ingenuity, both to experiments in mechanics and to inventions. While some of his designs are far-fetched, others are quite practicable.

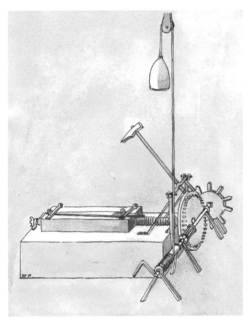

To take just one example among Da Vinci's drawings, there is one (*a copy of which is shown here*) of a machine that would cut the grooves in a file, while advancing the file blank a suitable distance on each stroke. This was a simple and elegant device, which guaranteed a regular spacing of file grooves that were previously cut by hand.

We cannot be certain that Leonardo invented every machine he sketched. Some of the machines he drew may well have existed already, and he was either recording them as good ideas for future reference or trying to improve on machines that he had seen or read about. In any event, the fact that workable drawings have come down to us from him shows that advanced mechanical thinking was already happening in his time.

It must be emphasised, however, that most of the practical applications of mechanical principles in this age were done intuitively. The mechanisms that were built and used in industry were developed by trial and error.

As far as sharing of inventions went, just as is done today, industrial secrets were kept from prying eyes. It seems that Leonardo was always on the look-out for ideas, and kept a sharp eye out for useful mechanisms to sketch as soon as he got home. He was probably not the only person 'collecting' ideas in this fashion, possibly with a view to selling them to interested industrialists.

For most of history, there was slow progress towards a collective understanding of the mathematical relationships that underpin the principles of mechanics. Likely reasons for this were the fact that populations were small and isolated, languages differed from one region to another, and communications were primitive.

Another factor that may have slowed the sharing of knowledge was the need to keep potentially useful information a secret, to prevent it from being used against your own city-state in military confrontations. Even today, however peaceable people like to think they are, a large proportion of advances in technology occur as a result of searches for ways to stay ahead of possible rivals in a military sense.

The inquirers who contributed the most to the science of mechanics seemed to have operated in two distinct periods: firstly, in the ancient world, and secondly, during the time between approximately 1450 and 1850, according to Mach[2], who describes the contributions of some 30 thinkers in this latter period. For us now, looking back at their writings, their thinking is often ponderous and limited by a lack of useful vocabulary to describe the phenomena they were trying to understand. Also, many of them were overly fond of theorising and impressing their audiences with their long-winded mathematical and quasi-mathematical interpretations.

Among about 30 major contributors, two in particular stand out as eminently worthy of our attention. These were Galileo Galilei (1564 -1642) and Isaac Newton (1643 - 1727).

Isaac Newton   *Galileo Galilei*

These two men were true giants of intellect, able to turn their minds to investigating a huge variety of problems in physics, mathematics, astronomy and chemistry. They both made astonishing achievements, in several fields of science. The importance of their contributions to our present-day knowledge in many branches of science, including mechanics, cannot be over-emphasised.

Before Galileo, almost all the major investigators had concerned themselves with *statics*, that part of mechanics that deals with objects that don't move. Galileo was the first to do experiments and publish his findings in the science of *dynamics*. He studied the motion of falling objects, of projectiles, and of pendulums. He also began investigations into the strength of materials. He designed and built telescopes and recorded many revelatory astronomical observations with the use of his telescopes.

Galileo's teachings were greatly appreciated by the scientific world at the time, but his notes had to be sneaked out of Italy, as he was under house arrest, subject to the displeasure of the immensely powerful Catholic church, which did its best to suppress any ideas contrary to the scriptures. The account by Sobel[3] of the way the Catholic Church suppressed the observations of Galileo is as horrific as any fiction. Students of today would do well to reflect on the privilege we have of being free from such restrictions on thought.

Isaac Newton, perhaps more than any other individual, pulled together the sum of the knowledge of previous contributors and formulated the laws of mechanics which we still find valid today, and which form the basis of any modern study of mechanics for engineering. These laws continue to stand up to all our experimental evidence.

In the 20th century, Einstein and others took physics to new levels, beyond what was evident to most people's imagination, and introduced the concept of relativity. Some observers are of the opinion that these new ideas have altered our conception of mechanics to the point where the way that Galileo and Newton interpreted the workings of the universe has become obsolete.

However, while pure scientists may incline to this opinion, the Newtonian view of the universe is still relied upon by engineers.

The reason for this is that differences between a relativistic universe and a Newtonian interpretation of our universe only become noticeable when objects are moving at or near the speed of light. Such an event is unlikely to be encountered by the average engineer or piece of equipment. It is therefore completely justifiable, for virtually all engineering purposes, to employ the conception of the physical world that prevailed in the time of Newton.

How the science of mechanics fits into engineering

The work of the engineer requires, on the one hand, a creative approach to solving problems, and on the other, the ability to source and apply records of accumulated knowledge that will ease that process. To take just one example:

Engineers have studied the behaviour of beams under load. They have noted the effects of different loading patterns on beams, and have made measurements to relate deflection (changes in the shape of a beam) with stress (force per unit area within the material).

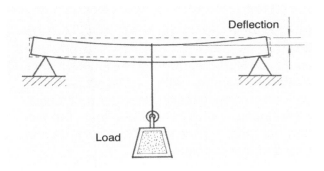

All this information has been summarised in mathematical form, so that whenever a beam is used, we may perform calculations that will help us to predict what size and type of beam we should be using in a given application. This is only one of many thousands of applications of the science of mechanics.

A knowledge of mechanics can assist us in such varied ways as these random examples show:

- predicting how far a projectile will fly,
- determining the right size flywheel for a machine,
- designing a boat to be stable in the water,
- designing the optimum suspension system for a racing car,
- choosing an appropriate structural design for building a bridge, and
- designing the turbine blades for a jet engine.

Almost every object or process that we use, and often take for granted, owes its existence and its refinement to someone's application of the principles of mechanics.

This is true of objects as small as a corkscrew and as large as a space station. It is also true of processes such as the utilisation of energy to perform work. Every propulsion system ever used relies on the principles of mechanics.

Having a solid grasp of basic mechanics enables us to make intelligent choices when designing any structure, machine or product to ensure that it will be functional, safe and enduring. The more we know about the science of mechanics, the better is the chance that a solution we propose to an engineering problem will work.

Is there much to learn
in order to master basic mechanics?

Actually, no. You have probably already got a basic ability to apply some of the principles of mechanics, from the intuitive knowledge you acquired during play as a child, and from trying to build household-scaled projects in your garage.

What you will be doing in a course in mechanics is merely formalising a whole lot of information of which you already have an intuitive grasp.

Most people get through life quite well on an intuitive knowledge of how the physical world works, acquired by experience. For example, when you take a curve on a bicycle, you lean automatically. There is a scientific explanation of why you need to lean, but you can still ride a bicycle without ever having heard of this principle.

It is quite normal that people operate many machines without really understanding how they work. In a high-tech world, the workings of many commonly-used devices are beyond the understanding of all but specialists. The average person doesn't know how a bathroom scale or a mobile phone or a television monitor works, yet they use them every day.

The engineer, however, needs to know a little more than the average person. If we want to be the *originators* of technologies, we need to understand exactly *why* and *how* things work, so that we can make them work for us.

We don't have to know how everything works, because that is impossible, but we do need to know the essential principles upon which most devices function, in the event that we will one day specialise and need to become conversant with a particular technology.

In which fields of engineering is a knowledge of mechanics essential?

Most working engineers tend to specialise so narrowly that, while they might know an impressive amount about the work they deal with daily, they might know very little about the work of engineers in some other fields. However, there is one science that almost all of them need to be conversant with: mechanics.

There is a vast array of specialist fields of work in engineering. You can get some idea of just how extensive this array is, by examining the following list of only *some* of the world's major industries, presented here in no particular order:

- manufacturing of household appliances and products
- mining and ore refinement
- production of metals for use in industry
- production of fibrous products such as rope and textiles
- processing of food and chemical products
- space exploration
- power generation and supply
- development and use of renewable energy sources
- water purification and supply, including desalination
- vehicle and aircraft manufacture
- development of new materials
- construction of roads, buildings, bridges, dams and piers
- information technology
- robotics
- shipbuilding and boat-building
- production of medical equipment
- production of industrial machinery, including earth-moving equipment and cranes

- timber and board production
- plastics moulding
- tool-making
- stone quarrying and cutting and polishing
- manufacture of ceramic products, including bricks, tiles and crockery
- instrument-making
- recovery, refinement and provision of oil and gas
- development of products for defence, security and surveillance
- production of agricultural machinery
- paper-making and printing
- manufacture of electronic goods and household appliances
- production of glass and products made from it

With the possible exception of certain branches of information technology, an understanding of basic mechanics is essential knowledge for technical personnel in *every single one* of these fields of engineering. Notice that no distinction is being made between the traditional divisions of engineering into mechanical, civil, and electrical. Even within these divisions, the actual work you end up doing may be so different from that of another engineer who trained in the same branch of engineering, that the two of you might know almost nothing about each other's specialisations.

As can be imagined from the breadth of the above list of industries, a course in basic mechanics cannot possibly cover every situation you are likely to encounter as an engineer.

However, such a course *can* cover all the *principles* of mechanics that you are ever likely to use, because there is only a small number of principles that need to be understood. It may surprise you to learn how *few* principles need to be learnt to provide a comprehensive grasp of mechanics. You will get a clear picture of the principles that make up the science of mechanics, from the subsequent chapter on concepts, quantities and principles in mechanics.

Why mechanics
remains an essential field of science

In today's world, we are surrounded by electronic devices and engines that work by burning fuel, or by using electricity. We also know that there are processes in industry that make use of such sophisticated developments as wi-fi, laser technology, computerised control systems, plasma cutters, 3-D printing, nanotechnology and robotics.

With all this advanced technology around us, it can be hard to keep in perspective

the fact that, for thousands of years, *all* machinery was *entirely* mechanical.

It is only comparatively recently, for the last 250 years or so, that we have seen the widespread use of machines that made use of combustible fossil fuels. And only for the last 150 years have we had electricity at our disposal.

Before then, every machine in existence was based solely on the application of the laws of mechanics. Besides those few that were powered by water and wind, nearly all early machines were powered either by animals, or by humans.

You could see every part of such a machine and figure out what its function was. Better still, if you knew something about working with wood and copper and iron and leather, you could repair or replace any defective part. It was comparatively easy to be an engineer. Regrettably, this is no longer the case.

Personal transporter with computerised control system.

Very seldom will you find a machine today whose functioning is entirely mechanical. There are some notable exceptions, like the bicycle, the sail boat, the hand loom, the spinning wheel, and certain hand tools used in woodwork and the kitchen.

The design of modern machinery and products requires us to combine a knowledge of mechanics with a knowledge of other sciences. These include thermodynamics (the study of heat and energy), electricity, electronics, hydraulics (the study of the use of liquids to transmit forces), pneumatics (the study of the use of compressed air to transmit forces) and modern materials science.

However, despite all the advances made in the adjacent fields of science, that are essential for engineering projects in today's world, whenever a machine part has to function, *all the laws of mechanics still apply to it.*

For example, if you want to build a robot, it is not sufficient for its control circuitry to work. You have to make sure that the power reaches the limbs, that the components of the limbs are strong enough, that the leverages within the limbs are suited to the forces those limbs have to exert, and that the joints function properly.

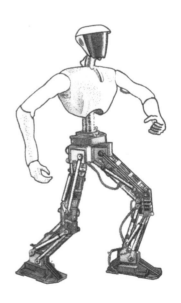

Artist's rendition of the prototype CHARLI-2 robot developed by Virginia Tech

Furthermore, you have to ensure that movements made by the robot do not result in its instability. All these functions are purely mechanical. The laws of mechanics are still the basis for anything mechanical to work. That is why we study mechanics.

In the chapter that follows, we will examine the types of knowledge about mechanics that each person needs in order to apply the science of mechanics to real problems. You will see that you need:

- Most importantly, the common sense that results from your own observations of the physical world,
- An understanding of formally defined concepts such as 'mass', 'displacement' and 'velocity', and
- An overview of the small number of major principles and laws that seem to govern the interaction between forces and physical objects.

Sources

1 Hodge, Trevor. Roman Aqueducts and Water Supply. London: Duckworth, 2002[2] p 371)

2 Mach, Ernst: The Science of Mechanics: a critical and historical account of its development: Chicago: The Open Court Publishing Company, 1919.

3 Sobel, Dava. Galileo's Daughter: A drama of science, faith and love. London: Fourth Estate, 1999.

Chapter 2

Concepts, quantities, principles and laws

- *Degrees of formality in knowledge patterns around mechanics*
- *Informally observed trends*
- *Mechanical concepts and quantities,*
- *Mechanical principles and laws*
- *Additional definitions necessary to the study of mechanics*
- *Words and concepts related to the word 'mechanics'*

Degrees of formality in knowledge patterns around mechanics

A knowledge pattern is a set of ideas, associations and memories that we carry, that define what we know about some topic. The study of mechanics is based on a small number of fundamental empirical knowledge patterns that humans have collectively accumulated about the behaviour of the physical world around us.

'Empirical' means: 'determined by experimental evidence', namely, a result confirmed by observation and testing, not by simply theorising.

While theorising has indeed assisted us to clarify certain mechanical principles, the results of that theorising have to be matched by observations in practice, or else they are worth nothing.

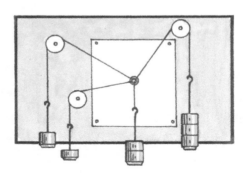

Apparatus to confirm by experiment the validity of the polygon of forces

We can classify knowledge patterns associated with mechanics into three groups, according to their degree of formality:

- *Informally observed trends that are the result of personal experience;*
- *Mechanical concepts: formally defined ideas in mechanics that allow us to understand exactly what other engineers and scientists are talking about, and*
- *Principles and Laws: relationships between certain mechanical concepts, that appear to hold true universally.*

Informally observed trends

The most basic knowledge patterns we have relating to mechanics are trends and consequences that we notice, from personal observation. For example, every time we drop an object, it falls towards the ground. That's a trend we will observe, no matter how many times we drop an object to see if it acts in the same way.

Observed trends are mechanical consequences that anybody could have noticed, without necessarily making measurements or putting numbers to them.

Some other first-hand observed trends, include, for example: when you heat a metal object, it expands; if you bend a wooden stick progressively, eventually it snaps. If you tie a knot in a shoelace, and walk around, eventually the knot tends to work loose. If a car runs into a wall, a lot of damage will result to both. If you boil water, steam comes off it.

Having such knowledge patterns is vital to your development as an engineer. The more you have noticed and internalised about the behaviour of the natural world, the better you can put to practical use what you learn from any person, or from any book.

Your own collection of 'observed trends' is the most useful tool you are ever going to have when designing anything mechanical. The thoughts that need to occur to you in the process of shaping a design cannot be found in

Detail from an 18th century engraving depicting James Watt wondering about the possible uses of steam.

any book. They fit into the realm of common sense, which is essentially the ability to anticipate the potential consequences of any particular action.

If you aspire to have some active part in technical decision-making, even without exposure to formal mechanics, you should be capable of thoughts like the following:

- *I wonder if that's going to be strong enough.*
- *We have to make sure it doesn't overbalance.*
- *I can see that this wheel is going to slip. I'll have to fix that.*
- *We need more weight on the back wheels.*
- *The belt is stretching, that's the problem.*
- *For this purpose, glass will be hard enough, but maybe too brittle.*
- *At this rate, that shaft is soon going to twist right off.*
- *It's looking too heavy. Where can I cut down weight?*
- *We are going to need a cover, or else sand is going to get into the workings.*

It is thoughts like these that initiate and shape a new design, and also form a starting point for your approach to solving a problem with an existing piece of equipment. Once such thoughts have occurred to you, it is often possible to apply an appropriate formal mechanical principle, and to do a check, with appropriate calculations, to discover more precisely what is needed. However, if you don't have these thoughts in the first place, you are not even going to be able to start troubleshooting an existing design, let alone produce an original design.

No design project ever starts with a calculation. Mechanical design and mechanical troubleshooting both start with intuition, based on experience. Intuition has been defined as the ability to understand something without the need for conscious reasoning. In other words, the process whereby your mind comes to a definite conclusion about some issue without having to go through discrete individual thoughts in a logical sequence to arrive at that conclusion.

No project ever ends with a calculation, either. When you have finished building a device, no matter whether it is simple or complex, there is no calculation, or set of calculations, that can appraise it from every point of view. The way we evaluate a project depends on us having an overall sense of the appropriateness of its function, its aesthetics, its cost, and the consequences of its operation for the environment. This sense comes with experience, and keen observation.

This author once heard a mechanical design lecturer telling students: 'If your design *looks* right, it probably *is* right.' That was a revelatory moment. You can calculate yourself to a standstill if you like, but intuition is the starting point and finishing point of all design.

Testing your understanding of mechanical consequences

Here follow some simple exercises that test your understanding of mechanical consequences, from your own experience. These exercises require no calculations. They are suitable to be discussed in a small group, after each member has attempted to answer the questions.

Exercise 1.

Stone	a	b	c	d	e
Diameter [mm]	10	20	30	40	50
Mass [grams]	1.5	12	40	94	185

You have five small stones, all approximately spherical and with the same density.

a. Which one could you throw the furthest? .... Why?

b. Which one could you throw the least far? .... Why?

Exercise 2

A heavy solid metal cylinder is dropped onto a wooden plank supported by 2 bricks resting on a concrete floor. The plank is not attached to the bricks.

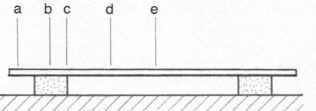

- The cylinder will be likely to bounce the highest if it hits at..........
- It will be most likely to crack a brick if it hits at...........
- It will be most dangerous to bystanders if it hits at.....
- It will be most likely to break the plank if it hits at.......

Exercise 3

The engraving shown below was drawn by a European traveller returning from China, possibly in the 18th century. Inspect the engraving, and try to answer the questions that follow.

1. What seems to be the purpose of the device illustrated in this engraving?

2. How does it work?

3. Are the men supposed to turn the rotating pole forwards, as one would pedal a bicycle, or backwards?

4. Could you suggest an improvement to this device? Sketch out your idea/s for these improvements.

Exercise 4

The device shown below: What is its purpose? What is it being used for in this particular instance? How does it work?

If you can answer questions of the kind presented above, you have got what it takes, in terms of your own experience and the trends you have observed informally, to engage with the science of mechanics, and to benefit from acquiring more formalised knowledge.

Formal mechanical concepts

In our approach to understanding mechanics, it is necessary to define certain *concepts,* to assist us to think about and communicate about the way in which mechanical objects and forces interact.

A concept is a constructed idea that describes and encompasses a set of other ideas. For example, the idea of 'mass' is a concept. When an engineer talks about 'mass' then other engineers need to understand exactly what he or she is talking about. This means that the concept of 'mass' requires a formal definition.

In the course of our involvement with mechanics, we will have to become familiar with approximately 20 to 30 mechanical concepts. Some of these are purely descriptive, while others lend themselves to measurement.

Descriptive mechanical concepts

These are mechanical concepts that can be defined without necessarily involving measurement. We need a clear idea of what these concepts represent, or else we cannot work with them to get to the point where calculations may serve us.

Most of the examples on the short list that follows, you ought to have encountered in your general reading and in school science.

Equilibrium	**Buoyancy**	**Scalar**	**Component**
Friction	**Units**	**Vector**	**Liquid**
Inertia	**Resultant**	**Space**	**Motion**

These descriptive concepts will be defined and explained where needed, in later chapters.

Mechanical concepts that are also known as 'quantities'

The next class of mechanical concepts includes those that are not only able to be defined, but are also able to be *measured*. If any phenomenon is measurable, we call it a 'quantity'. For example, 'time' is a quantity, because the duration of a period of time can be measured.

A quantity must be specified by stating its value and its units. For example, the mass of an object might be measured as 150 kg. The *value* is the figure 150, describing the magnitude, and the *units*, in this case, are kilograms.

The table below includes some of the most important quantities you will encounter in mechanics, together with their basic S.I. units. *(The SI system,* Système Internationale, *is used almost universally to measure quantities. There is more about this system in the chapter on the use of numbers in engineering.)*

Quantity	Units
mass	kilogram [kg]
time	second [s]
length	metre [m]
force	newton [N]
weight (a force)	newton [N]
velocity	[m/s]
acceleration	[m/s^2]
Force moment (turning effort produced by a force)	[Nm]
torque (equivalent to a force moment)	[Nm]
area	[m^2]
volume	[m^3]

density	[kg/m^3]
mechanical work	joules [Nm]
energy (the stored capacity to perform mechanical work)	joules [Nm]
power (the rate at which mechanical work is performed)	watts [Nm/s]
frequency (the number of events per second)	hertz [Hz]
pressure (force per unit area)	pascals (Pa) = [N/m^2]
stress (force per unit area)	pascals (Pa) = [N/m^2]
momentum (how hard it is to stop an object moving)	[kg.m/s]
angle	radians [rad]
angular velocity	radians/second [rad/s]
angular acceleration	[rad/s^2]
angular momentum	[kg.m^2/s]
mass moment of inertia	[kg.m^2]

The three 'fundamental' quantities in mechanics: length, mass and time

In the table above, if one examines the units of any of the quantities, one can see that some of the units can be expressed in terms of other units. For example, velocity has units of length per time, so length and time are more fundamental quantities than velocity. However, length cannot be defined in terms of anything simpler than itself. Length is thus regarded as one of the three 'fundamental quantities'. The same applies to time, and mass.

Therefore: length, mass, and time are called the *fundamental* quantities of mechanics. They are so called because:

1 All the other quantities in the above table can be defined in terms of combinations of these three, and

2 The essential nature of each of the three fundamental quantities can only be defined on the basis of our experience and intuition.

The quantities that are not fundamental are called derived quantities, as they can be derived from the fundamental ones.

Length, or distance

'Length' is a measure of how far apart two given points are. The basic S.I. unit of length is the metre.

In 1889 the length of a metre was chosen, based on what was thought to be one ten-millionth of the distance from the North Pole to the Equator, measured along the surface of the Earth. A bar of a platinum-iridium alloy was made to this dimension, and kept in an archive at constant temperature. The length of this bar became the standard that defined one metre exactly.

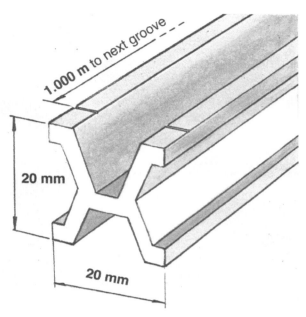

The cross-section of the platinum-iridium bar used to define the standard metre, designed for maximum rigidity

The modern definition of a metre has been adjusted slightly from this value. It was thought more reliable to link the definition of a metre to a universal constant, in this case the speed of light in a vacuum. The length of a metre is now defined by redefining the measured speed of light in a vacuum and declaring that speed to be exactly 299792458 metres per second.

Mass

There are two generally accepted ways of defining mass. Both of them make sense, but neither of them is at all practical. The first one defines mass as 'the amount of matter that an object contains'. However, we cannot usefully apply this definition to measure the mass of an object, because there is no way of measuring directly how much matter is contained in an object. If you could count atoms and subatomic particles, you could get around this problem. However, up to now, even with the best advances in physics at our disposal, such a task remains impossible.

Another definition says that the mass of an object is evident from the amount of inertia a body possesses, namely how much it resists being accelerated by external forces. This definition, while valid in principle, also does not provide a useful means of determining mass, because it is almost impossible to measure the force exerted on an accelerating body by an external agent, while measuring the acceleration at the same time.

The only practical way we have for deducing a value for the mass of an object is by measuring its *weight*. This has been done for thousands of years, and continues to be done daily wherever mass needs to be measured.

Gold rings being weighed in ancient Egypt. Copied from a wall painting in a tomb in Thebes, original painted around 1400 B.C.

If a weighing scale shows that you 'weigh' 78 kg, it means that you experience the same force of gravitational attraction to the Earth that any other 78 kg mass would experience, at that particular location. It follows that your mass must be 78 kg.

The basic SI unit of mass is the kilogram, [kg]. This might seem puzzling, for it would appear that the basic unit ought to be the gram. After all, 'gram' sounds like the root word, and a kilogram is a multiple of the gram. At an early stage in the development of the SI system, the gram *was* considered a suitable basic unit. However, the gram turns out to be an inconvenient size, far too small for most purposes. As an indication of the magnitude of the gram, note that one sheet of A4 printer paper has a mass of approximately 4 grams.

Besides the fact that the gram is inconveniently small, there are two practical considerations that make the kilogram an ideal base unit of mass. Firstly, there is the very useful fact that 1 kg of water occupies a volume of 1 litre, equivalent to one cubic decimetre. Oddly, the litre is not listed as an official unit in the SI system, but is one of those units that is accepted into common usage alongside the formal SI units, on account of its practicality. Secondly, the kilogram is involved in the definition of the newton as a unit of force (see the definition of force below), and so the kilogram, rather than the gram, is now the accepted base unit of mass.

Time

Time is understood by virtue of the fact that some events happen *after* others. In the Newtonian view of the universe, the passage of time is assumed to be steady and continuous. Despite protestations by scientists that time is really pliable, Newton's interpretation is, for all practical purposes, perfectly acceptable for virtually all engineering situations likely to be encountered on Earth.

Our sense of time arose from the way the world around us functions: we experience cycles of day and night, and seasons. Measurement of these involved nothing more than counting.

When it became expedient to divide time into smaller portions, various methods were devised to keep track of elapsed time. Among these were sundials, hourglasses, candles with markings, and water-clocks, which depended on the slow release of water through a small hole in a container.

Clockwork mechanisms were developed around the 12th century. In the 1920s the quartz watch was invented. These get their timing from an electronic oscillator regulated by a quartz crystal. This process has become standard for most time measurement. International time standards are now set by atomic clocks, which work by using the electronic transition frequency of particular atoms to keep time.

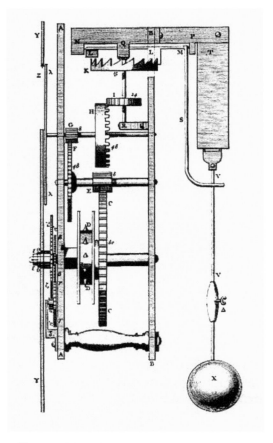

Illustrated here is the second pendulum clock built by its inventor, Christiaan Huygens, in 1673. Huygens was an internationally respected scientist who made contributions in the fields of astronomy, mechanics and optics, as well as in horology. This clock he claimed to be accurate to within 10 seconds in a day.

The basic SI unit of time is the second, [s], which is traditionally defined as one 60th part of a minute, itself defined as one 60th part of an hour, of which there are (by common consent) exactly 24 in a solar day, namely the time for the Earth to make one rotation on its own axis, relative to the sun. That is, the time from the sun being directly overhead at a given meridian, to it being overhead again on the next occasion. Accordingly, there are 864000 seconds in one solar day.

However, this definition of the second has been adjusted by scientists, as the rotational velocity of the Earth is steadily, though minutely, decreasing, which means that the duration of a solar day is correspondingly (minutely) increasing. Scientists needed a measure of time that is unvarying. The duration of one second is now defined as a precise number of periods of a certain frequency of radiation from a caesium atom.

Such precision need not unduly concern the average person. Every 100 years the duration of a solar day lengthens by approximately 1.4 milliseconds. At this rate, it will take more than seventy-one thousand years for the duration of a solar day to increase by one present-day second. This discrepancy will not be discernible on any timepiece that you are ever likely to use. Nor is it significant enough to compel you to update your calculations, no matter what age you attain.

Force: the fourth 'fundamental' quantity in mechanics

A force is a push or a pull action that attempts to change the state of motion or the shape of a body. The concept of force is absolutely fundamental to mechanics.

Since mechanics is all about the interaction of forces with materials, if there were no such thing as a force, there would be no science of mechanics.

Then, why isn't force considered a fundamental quantity? Actually, in one sense, it *is*.

The SI unit of force is the newton, named after Sir Isaac Newton, and given the symbol 'N'. One newton is defined as that force which will impart an acceleration of 1 m/s² to a mass of 1 kg. In terms of this definition, the newton may be viewed as a derived unit, as opposed to a fundamental unit. However, one could equally argue that if the newton were to be considered a fundamental unit, we might well define the kilogram in terms of the newton, namely, as that mass which would be given an acceleration of 1 m/s² by a force of 1 N.

Whichever way you look at it, the quantity called force ranks as vitally as do those of length, mass and time, in the science of mechanics.

A subsequent chapter in this book deals extensively with how to work with forces.

Surprisingly, hardly anyone except engineers and scientists is familiar with the unit of force called the newton. The average citizen makes no distinction between mass and weight, and is content to think about forces in terms of kilograms and tonnes, which are both units of mass. It is understandable that lay people should blur this distinction, for the very reason that it is only possible to compare the masses of objects by knowing what those objects weigh.

The remainder of the derived mechanical quantities in the preceding table will be fully defined in the chapters that deal with them.

Principles and laws of mechanics

Archimedes

What's the difference between a principle and a law? Essentially, there is no mutually exclusive difference. Some hold that a principle is a knowledge pattern that is always true, and can be described in words, whereas a law is a principle that is so reliable that we can use a mathematical equation to relate the variables involved.

However, if one uses this distinction, Newton's First Law (see below) should rightly be called a principle. Therefore, we shall scrap any distinction, and simply accept the historical names given to these formalised knowledge patterns.

Governing the science of mechanics is a total of probably fewer than 20 principles and laws. Below is given a brief description of nine of these principles and laws: the ones that are most useful to us in the study of basic mechanics.

The list given below is not arranged in any particular order, because there cannot be some principles that take precedence over others. For any principle or law to be valid, it must apply all the time, without exceptions, alongside any other principles and laws that are valid.

Archimedes' Principle

When a solid body is immersed in a fluid, it experiences a buoyancy force, which is an upward force exerted on it by the surrounding fluid.

Archimedes was the first to understand that the magnitude of the buoyancy force is equal to the weight of the displaced fluid.

He devised this principle as a result of grappling with a vexing question that occupied his king: namely, to tell him for certain whether a crown that was claimed to be made of solid gold really was made of pure gold, or whether it was alloyed with other metals. The practical uses of this principle are explained in the chapter on buoyancy.

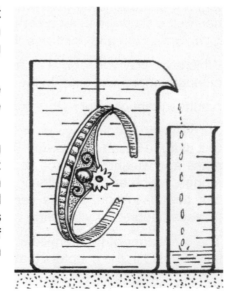

The Parallelogram Law for the addition of vectors

A vector quantity is one that has to be defined by specifying *both* magnitude and direction. Forces, velocities and accelerations are examples of vectors. This law describes the method of determining the resultant of two vectors of the same type acting in the same plane. The addition is performed by arranging the two vectors in the form of a parallelogram, with the vectors to be added forming two adjacent sides. The resultant is represented by the diagonal of the parallelogram.

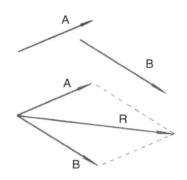

Like all the other laws, this one is based on experimental evidence. The parallelogram law will be explained in the chapter on forces.

Newton's First Law: equilibrium prevails until disturbed.

A body that is in equilibrium will remain in equilibrium unless it is acted on by an external force.

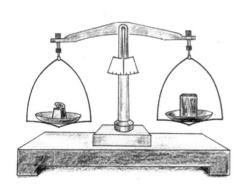

Equilibrium means 'balance'. The word is derived from the Latin word that describes the state of balance of a pair of weighing scales (called libra).

An object is in equilibrium if it would carry on doing whatever it is doing unless acted on by a force.

There are three states of movement that are considered to represent equilibrium for an object:

- *standing still relative to Earth, or*
- *moving at constant velocity in a straight line, or*
- *spinning with constant angular velocity around an axis passing through its centre of mass.*

An object that is accelerating in any way, moving in the path of a curve, spinning around an axis that does not coincide with its centre of mass, or being deformed, is *not* in equilibrium.

It is important to be able to recognise whether or not equilibrium applies in a given situation, because all problems in mechanics can be treated with one of three approaches, depending on whether they deal with equilibrium, acceleration, or are impact-related.

Newton's Second Law: relating force, inertia and acceleration

The mass of a body provides inertia, namely a resistance to changes in motion. When a force **F** attempts to accelerate a body of mass **m**, the acceleration, **a**, that results, will be greater in proportion to the force applied and smaller in proportion to the mass of the body.

This law is described by the well-known equation: **F = ma.** The law is easier to visualise if the equation is re-arranged as: **a = F/m.**

Newton's second law explains why adding passengers to a car reduces the acceleration of which the car is capable.

This Law is the basis of the chapter on linear accelerating systems.

Newton's Third Law: forces occur in opposing pairs

This law states that if two objects, A and B, are in contact, and A exerts a force on B, then B must be exerting an equal and opposite force on A. People often summarise this law with the slogan 'action equals reaction', which is a misleading phrase, because it leads one to imagine that the *effects* of the two forces on the respective objects are the same. However, while the forces are indeed equal and opposite, their effects are not.

There is the age-old conundrum about what happens when a mosquito flies into the windscreen of a speeding train. Can the forces they exert on one another be equal? Yes. They are, but the *effect* of that amount of force on the mosquito is sufficient to crush it, while the effect of the same amount of force on the train is utterly negligible.

The implications of Newton's 3rd Law will be explained in the chapter on forces.

Newton's Law of Gravitation

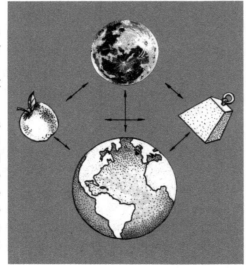

This is probably the law for which Newton is most famous, on account of the revelatory insights about gravity that he developed, which seemed to have escaped most observers before his time.

Newton observed that any two objects that possess mass, experience a mutual gravitational attraction. He suggested that the force of attraction that each of the two objects experiences is of the same magnitude, but opposite in direction. He also formulated a way of determining the magnitude of the gravitational force:

According to him, this force is proportional to the product of the masses, and inversely proportional to the square of the distance between them.

This relationship is described by the equation $F = (G\ m_1m_2)/r^2$, where G is a constant known as 'the universal gravitation constant', m_1 and m_2 are the masses of the two objects, and 'r' is the distance between the centres of mass of the two objects.

A particular case of gravitational attraction is *weight*. The weight of an object is the gravitational force exerted *on* the object *by* the Earth.

An analysis of the concept of weight and some of the limitations of Newton's Law of Gravitation are discussed in the chapter on forces.

The Law of Conservation of Energy

This Law states that the total amount of energy contained in a *closed system* (defined further on in the present chapter) is fixed and accountable: the energy that is present may change in form, or pass from one object to another within the system, but the total amount remains constant.

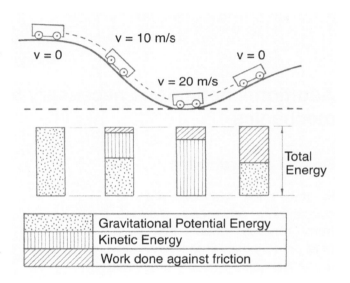

Gravitational Potential Energy	
Kinetic Energy	
Work done against friction	

See more about this Law in the chapter on work, energy and power.

The Law of Conservation of Momentum

The momentum of an object is defined to be the product of its mass and its velocity. It is convenient to think of the momentum of an object as the extent to which it is difficult to stop the motion of that object.

An ocean-going ship moving at walking pace has a huge amount of momentum, on account of its large mass. Likewise, a small bullet, travelling at great speed, has a large momentum, on account of its high velocity.

Momentum may be gained and lost by individual objects within a system, but the total amount of momentum within a closed system does not change. This Law is explained in the chapter on linear momentum.

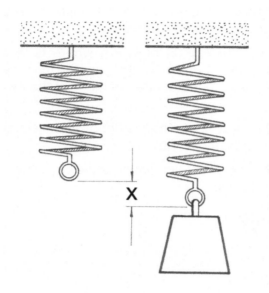

Hooke's Law

The extension of a spring is proportional to the force applied, provided the force is not great enough to extend the spring beyond its elastic range. An object is behaving elastically when it returns to its original shape after a force that caused it to change its shape is removed. Robert Hooke, a contemporary of Isaac Newton, studied this law in relation to springs, but it also applies to other solid objects, such as bars and beams, in the elastic range of their behaviour.

Some practical applications of this law are described in the chapter on work, energy and power.

Additional definitions necessary to the study of mechanics

Spatial co-ordinates

In this book we will not be considering advanced theories from physics about the way time and space are considered to be flexible. For all practical purposes, as we have seen, in the engineering that takes place on or near the surface of the Earth, the Newtonian concept of time and space is completely adequate.

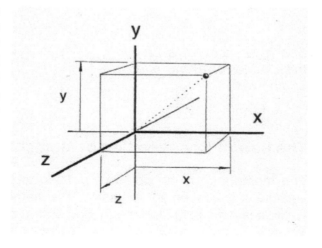

In the Newtonian view of the universe, space is considered to be a three-dimensional extending volume, within which the position of any particle can be defined by linear dimensions relative to a chosen fixed point (the origin), along three orthogonal axes. It is customary to name these axes respectively the x-, y- and z- axes.

(Another way of describing the position of an object in space, is by using polar co-ordinates. However, that method will not be used in this book.)

Some convenient fictions that assist us to define and clarify what we mean in mechanics

Occasionally, to assist us in organising our ideas about physical objects, we make use of some further concepts that are *convenient fictions.* This means that such concepts do not occur in practice, but are useful approximations to something that might be found in practice. These include the *particle*, the *element*, the *rigid body*, and the *closed system.*

A particle, also known as a point mass.

A *particle* is defined to be a small amount of concentrated matter, occupying a single point in space. In practice, of course, no such thing exists. Perhaps the closest thing to a particle (on Earth, that is, not in a Black Hole) is a small dense sphere, like a steel ball-bearing. An object may be considered to be a particle if its dimensions are small enough not to allow it any potential for rotating when acted on by forces.

An element (not in the sense of a *chemical* element)

An element is a conceptualised small portion of the material of a solid body, or of an area, specifically defined in terms of its dimensions and location, in order to derive some general characteristic of the whole body by the methods of integration.

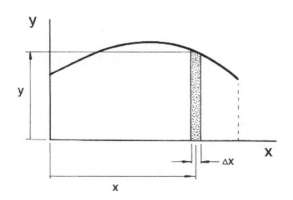

For example, suppose we need to determine an expression for the area under a curve that is defined by an equation. We could divide the area into vertical strips, called 'elements', each of height 'y' and width 'Δx'.

Letting the width of Δx become infinitesimally small, tending to 'dx', we can perform an integration to add up the areas of all the elements between two given limits.

There are a number of occasions in mechanics where it is useful to analyse the characteristic properties of a whole object by means of a similar process, starting off by dividing the object into elements.

A rigid body

A *rigid body* is a solid object that is assumed not to change shape under the action of forces. In practice, no matter how hard or inflexible an object is, when acted on by forces, any object *will* change shape, even if only microscopically. However, if an object is inflexible enough and the forces acting on it are not large enough to deform the object significantly, then for all practical purposes we can regard the object as rigid.

A closed system

A *closed system* in mechanics is a collection of objects (whether solid, liquid or gas) that are presumed not to cross the boundary of an imagined "bubble" of space. For the purposes of making an analysis, it is sometimes convenient to pretend that nothing crosses the boundary, either into, or out of, a closed system. Again, this is one of those necessary conveniences to the logical thought process, which is not easily replicated in reality.

For example, consider a man sitting in a motionless canoe on the still waters of a lake, holding a small rock close to his chest.

If he throws the rock forwards, the canoe moves backwards. We can describe a closed system consisting of the man, the canoe, and the rock, to help us analyse the changes in motion that occur between these objects, using the law of the conservation of momentum.

However, in reality, at the time of the throw, all of these objects are in contact with air, and one of them is also in contact with the water of the lake, so the system of interacting objects is not truly isolated.

Words and concepts related to the word 'mechanics'

Using the right word for the right thing is an important part of what one learns in any field of study. You will be introduced to all the appropriate terms that are needed, in the chapters that follow. However, to begin with, it is important to learn the distinctions between various words that are related to the word 'mechanics'.

Our word 'mechanics' is derived from the ancient Greek word 'mekhos', which means a 'device', namely something that helps us to accomplish a task.

A number of other words that you are likely to encounter derive from the basic word 'mekhos'. You probably know most of them, but it is useful to define them, anyway.

Machine ....A device for transforming force or energy into a more usable form.

Machinist ....A person who operates a machine.

Mechanic ....A person who fixes and maintains machines.

Mechanical ....An adjective describing a device that works with moving parts and physical materials (whether solid, liquid or gaseous).

Mechanics .....The science of understanding how the physical world behaves.

Mechanism ....A device, with linked parts, that changes the magnitude, velocity or direction of an applied force. Usually part of a machine.

Mechanist ......An expert on the science of mechanics.

Mechanistic ...An adjective applied to things that are *not* mechanical, indicating that they are being treated as if they were as simple as physical mechanisms.

Conclusion

The present chapter has outlined some of the most important

* *concepts,*
* *quantities,*
* *principles, laws and*
* *some vocabulary*

necessary to a study of engineering mechanics.

Each principle will be explained in further detail in the subsequent individual chapter to which it applies.

Later on, with some practice, you will be able to recognise the types of situation to which each of these respective principles are relevant.

Before we go on to start using the principles, we will need to clarify some basic rules about the use of numbers in engineering. Readers will need to gain a perspective on how to use numbers when calculations are required, and what degree of accuracy is appropriate. These important ground rules are dealt with in the chapter that follows.

Chapter 3

Working with numbers in engineering

- *Engineering notation, as opposed to scientific or ordinary notation*
- *The number of significant figures in a value*
- *Required format of answers for engineering purposes*
- *Loss of accuracy when rounding off numbers during a calculation*
- *The units that apply to mechanical quantities in the S.I. system*
- *The difference between precision and accuracy*
- *The limitations of precision in a primarily practical science*
- *Converting the units of quantities, e.g. miles per hour to metres per second*
- *Units preferred by engineers*

An engineering student needs to know how to write and interpret numbers for the purposes of engineering. At some stage in your career, you will be writing lab and other types of investigative reports, performing calculations, and showing the results of your calculations. It is essential to get to know the conventions.

Engineering notation, as opposed to scientific or ordinary notation

Any given number can be expressed in three ways: ordinary arithmetic notation, scientific notation, and engineering notation.

Ordinary arithmetic notation is what comes up on your calculator readout when you key in a sequence of digits. For example: 86.5 or 374.29 or 128502.972

Scientific notation is a way of writing a number in terms of multiples of powers of ten. For example: 1.284×10^4 or 4.932×10^{17} or 7.996×10^{-6}. In scientific notation, the aim is to express the number as compactly as possible. Only one digit is allowed in front of the decimal point, and any multiple of powers of 10 can be used.

Often, however, numbers expressed in scientific notation, though mathematically valid, are not conveniently practical for engineers to work with. For this reason, **engineering notation** was developed.

Consider the number, in ordinary notation: 154 300. A scientist would write it as 1.543×10^5, whereas an engineer would write it as 154.3×10^3. If both are mathematically correct, what's the difference, and why is there a difference?

In engineering notation, the aim is to have numbers expressed in terms of multiples of powers of ten, that describe groupings that represent other units in common use. For example:

Units of length: 1 metre = 10^3 mm and 1 kilometre = 10^3 m

Units of mass: 1 kg = 10^3 grams and 1 tonne = 10^3 kg

We can easily visualise the magnitudes of quantities in terms of these common units.

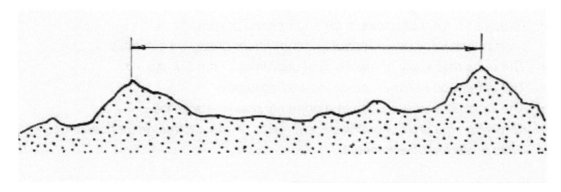

A practical example of the day-to-day impracticality of scientific notation: one could describe the distance between two given mountain peaks, using scientific notation, as 3.629×10^4 m. Though there is nothing mathematically wrong with this way of expressing the distance, how easy is it to picture this distance in your mind? It is much more practical to record the distance as 36.29×10^3 m, since 10^3 m = 1 km, and, from experience, we can easily imagine a distance of approximately 36 km.

In numbers written in scientific notation, one could find *any* multiples of powers of ten. But, in engineering notation, we *only* use powers of ten that are grouped in threes, such as 10^{-9}, 10^{-6}, 10^{-3}, 10^0, 10^3, 10^6, 10^9, and so on.

Examples of engineering notation:

A dimension of 4519 m would be written as 4.519×10^3 m. In this particular case the form of the number happens to be identical to the form it has when written in scientific notation.

A mass of 68020 kg would be written as 68.02×10^3 kg. Since 10^3 kg = 1 tonne, if we have any experience of the mass of 1 tonne, it is easy to visualise what this number represents.

A pressure of 185600 Pa would be written as 185.6×10^3 Pa, or 185.6 kPa.

A surface area of 0.7386 m² could be written as 738.6×10^{-3} m². However, in this case, writing the number in engineering notation is more complex than writing it in ordinary notation. Engineers prefer simplicity and practicality, so most would leave this number in ordinary arithmetic notation, as an area of 0.7386 m^2 is easy to visualise.

From the foregoing example, it is clear that it is not always necessary for engineers to represent numbers in formal engineering notation. A number only needs to be expressed in engineering notation when it is *larger than 1000 or smaller than 1/100*. For example, 234 800 would be written as 234.8 x 10^3 and 0.002348 would be written as 2.348 x 10^{-3}.

However, numbers in the following range of magnitudes can be left in *ordinary* notation, *exactly as they appear here*:

234.8   23.48   2.348   0.2348   0.02348

Exercise: Convert each of the following numbers to engineering notation (do not forget to retain the correct units: if the units are wrong, the answer is considered incorrect):

Given figure	In engineering notation	Given figure	In engineering notation
235801.82 m	235.80182 x 10^3 m	2.4567 x 10^7 watts	
48.2717 N/mm^2		1.5053 x 10^{-4}	
0.00907 N		3.5108 x 10^{21} miles	
500.065 kg		87.165 kg	
10371981 Pa		0.000003278	
0.00343 MW		456.321 x 10^8 km	

The number of significant figures in a value

Suppose you do a calculation and get an answer of 34.5105342 on your calculator. How should you write it down? Do you need all the digits after the decimal point? Do you need any of them? How many digits are appropriate in order to define the number? Such questions lead us to consider the importance of 'significant figures'.

A significant figure is a digit whose value helps to define the 'significant value' of a number, namely the value that defines its magnitude as observed for a particular purpose. Suppose two motor cars coming off a production line are weighed. The first car has a mass of 1400.002 kg, and the second has a mass of 1400.005 kg. For all practical purposes, these two cars may be considered to have the same mass, as the difference between them is not significant.

Depending on the accuracy that is needed from a number, in a particular context, one may specify differing numbers of significant figures to define the value of the number.

For example, if a country does a census and finds it has 44 362 098 citizens, every digit in this number is significant. This number has 8 significant figures. That's how many citizens there are, exactly. So, the census result needs to reflect 8 significant figures. However, when the media refer to this population in a report that is not related to the census, they are likely to describe the country's population as consisting of '44 million people'. For their purposes, only two significant figures are necessary.

So, which digits in a number are significant?

Rules for significant figures

a. All non-zero digits *are* significant: 6.8293 has 5 significant figures.

b. Zeroes between non-zero digits *are* significant: 1007 has 4 significant figures.

c. When there is no other digit but a zero before the decimal point, the zeroes to the left of the first non-zero digit, are *not* significant. They serve only to show the position of the decimal point: 0.00532 has 3 significant figures

d. Zeroes to the right of the last non-zero digit may or may not be significant, depending on the level of accuracy that is being implied: If you were told that the distance from town A to town B was 130 km, as a rough estimate, then the number 130 contains 2 significant figures. But, if you actually measured the distance and found it to be closer to 130 than to 131 or 129 km, then 130 has three significant figures. If you measure the mass of an object on a scale that reads to the nearest gram, and it indicates 430 grams exactly, then this number has three significant figures. But, if the scale was accurate to one tenth of a gram, and showed 430.0 g, this number has four significant figures.

Required format of answers, for engineering purposes

Suppose you determine, by calculation, that the mass of a concrete counterweight for a small crane needs to be 2096.97047 kg. It is very difficult to ensure that an object this large can be made with such accuracy. It is quite acceptable to express the required mass as 2097 kg, or even as 2100 kg, because, when the counterweight is eventually made, one would expect to find the mass differing from the desired value by a few kg either way. So, there is no point in including all the decimal places found in the originally computed number.

By rounding off the above number to 2097 kg, we have reduced the precision of it from nine to *four* significant figures. But, this does not represent a significant loss of accuracy, because, for most practical purposes in engineering, when we arrive at an answer as a result of calculations, presenting it to four significant figures *is completely accurate enough*.

You may be tempted to wonder what the use is of having ten digits in your calculator display, if we need only express answers to four significant figures. How accurate is an answer expressed to four significant figures?

An example: suppose you measure the length of a room that is approximately 10 metres long. How accurately can this distance be measured? Using a standard measuring tape, you can measure to the nearest mm. Supposing you read off the tape that the dimension you have measured is 10.324 m. This number has five significant figures. If you reduce it to four significant figures, it becomes 10.32 m. In doing so, what have we lost?

The accuracy has now been reduced by 4 mm, from a total amount of 10324 mm, which represents a percentage drop of $4 \div 10324 \times 100 = 0.039\%$, or 3.9 parts in ten thousand. What difference would this make to our interpretation of the 'correct' value of the dimension? Knowing how walls are built and plastered, it would be surprising if we got exactly the same value if we measured the distance between the same two opposite walls in two different places. If we measured it down the right hand wall instead of the left, we might easily obtain a figure that differed from the original measurement by more than 4 mm. So, for all practical purposes, it is accurate enough to say that this room is 10.32 m long.

If a fifth significant figure is recorded as a result of a calculation, and is incorrect by one unit, this represents an error of only one part in ten thousand.

For the greater majority of figures arrived at by calculation, it is sufficiently accurate to quote the result to four significant figures. As you will see below, there are several reasons why such a level of accuracy is completely acceptable.

Calculations that lead to choices among available options

Very often in engineering, the result of a calculation leads to the choosing of a suitable item from a catalogue. For example, from a design calculation you might determine that you need machine screws of diameter 7.608325 mm. But the catalogue does not list screws of intermediate sizes. It might list a 7 mm diameter screw and an 8 mm diameter one. So, you make a practical compromise, and choose screws of diameter 8 mm. If the application for which you need the screw has a safety consideration, you may even choose to use a screw much larger than needed, as a factor of safety. You may use a 9 or even a 10 mm screw. In situations like this, all the accuracy implied by the digits you recorded after the first decimal place, is rendered meaningless.

Again, suppose you determine the diameter of a wooden pole needed to carry a certain load. Your calculations show that this pole needs to have a diameter of 335.786 mm. It is doubtful if you can spare the resources to have a pole made to this exact specification. So, you would round off your result to the standard engineering format of four significant figures, namely 335.8 mm. Then, as happens in all practical situations, you have a look at the standard pole diameters that are available. The catalogue of the company providing the poles might show they have one pole size with diameters in the range from 300 to 330 mm, and another standard size ranging between 330 and 360 mm. To make sure the pole you get is strong enough, you would choose one from the range above that, namely 360 to 390 mm. So, of what use were the digits in your answer that came after the decimal point?

These are very practical considerations, encountered frequently in the daily life of engineers. However, one should not get the impression that all engineering calculations need only be 'rough and ready' approximations.

When is a high degree of accuracy essential?

There are certain situations in which great accuracy is necessary. For example, in computing the trajectory of a rocket, taking into account the effect of the diminishing fuel load on the rocket's acceleration, and the variation in air resistance as a function of its velocity. Here, the greatest possible accuracy must be maintained, and such accuracy can only be achieved by employing algorithms in a computer programme.

When is a high degree of accuracy not possible?

There are also cases where the use of four significant figures is more accurate than necessary. For example, when you determine the coefficient of friction between two given solid surfaces in the laboratory, try as you might, you cannot get exactly the same readings every time. After a lot of experimentation, you have to accept that this coefficient can only be determined reliably to one decimal place, and leave it at that.

The convention for calculation results used in this book

In this book we will use the convention of expressing all calculation results in engineering notation, rounded off to four significant figures, unless otherwise specified. Numbers with values between 1/100 and 1000 can be left in ordinary notation, rounded off to four significant figures.

Converting numbers from ordinary to engineering notation, with four significant figures

Given all the rules and guidelines mentioned above, how does one go about converting a number from ordinary notation to engineering notation?

Consider the number 4529572.43

First round it off to four significant figures. The number becomes 4530000.

Then, adjust the decimal point in jumps of three places at a time, starting from where it is, at the right hand end of the number. Showing the jumps in groups of three, we obtain

4.530.000.

To get to this value, we moved the decimal point six places to the left, so we have effectively divided by 10^6. Now we have to again multiply by 10^6, in order not to change the value of the number, so the number becomes 4.530×10^6.

In this particular result, the zero after the three is important, because it is in the fourth significant place. That zero implies that the number is closer to 4.530×10^6 than it is to 4.529×10^6 or 4.531×10^6. Without the zero, the implied value could range anywhere between 4.525×10^6 and 4.534×10^6.

Suppose you do a calculation and get an answer of 65.4 mm exactly. If you write 65.4 mm, everyone would know what you are talking about, so, from a practical point of view, your answer is not wrong. But, the strictly correct way of writing this, if it is to be written with four significant figures, is 65.40 mm. The zero after the 4 indicates that this number is not some slightly differing amount like 65.42 rounded down, or 65.39 rounded up, but *exactly* 65.40 mm.

What needs to be done if a number has a form like this: 0.0090738? Look at the part of the number where non-zero numerals begin. Keeping the initial zeroes, round off the significant figure part of the number to four significant figures, so, in this case: 0.009074.

Now, move the decimal point to the right, in jumps of three: from 0.009074 to 0.009.074. Having moved the decimal three places to the right, we have effectively multiplied by 1000. Now, to restore the number to its true value, we have to *divide* by 1000. This is accomplished by multiplying by 10^{-3}. So the number becomes 9.074×10^{-3}.

Exercise: in the table below: For each of the given quantities, first round it off to four significant figures, and then write it in engineering notation.

Given figure	Rounded to 4 significant figures	Expressed in engineering notation
3002.451	3002	3.002×10^3
4.8009812×10^5	4.801×10^5	480.1×10^3
17.6666666666	17.67	17.67
235.4672 m		
2.500063×10^7		
0.0031988 lb		
0.0000031 lb		
5301.034 kg		
122 731 681 Pa		
0. 00629 t		

Loss of accuracy when rounding off numbers during a calculation

When we reduce the number of significant figures in a *final answer* of a set of calculations, we reduce the accuracy of that answer. As we have seen, it is usually quite acceptable to do so, if the accuracy required of our answer is not critical. Which is the case in the vast majority of engineering situations.

However, care must be taken when rounding off numbers in the *intermediate* stages of a calculation, because the loss of accuracy can be compounded when using those intermediate results in further calculations.

Examples:

1. Multiply: 4398.34 × 6023.52

Retaining all the given digits, the product of these two numbers is 26493488.96. Rounding this off to four significant figures yields 26.49×10^6. If the two numbers are rounded off to four significant figures *before* multiplying them, we have 4398 × 6024 = 26493552, or 26.49×10^6. Here there is no discernible difference between the two results.

2. Add: 4398.34 + 6023.52

Retaining all the given digits, the sum of these two figures is 10421.86 Rounding this off to four significant figures yields 10.42×10^3. If the two numbers are rounded off to four significant figures *before* adding them, we have 4398 + 6024 = 10422, or 10.42×10^3. As with the multiplication above, there is no effective loss of accuracy.

3. Subtract: 6023.52 – 4398.34

Retaining all the given digits, the difference between these two figures is 1625.18. Rounding this off to four significant figures yields 1.625×10^3. If we round off the two numbers before subtracting them: 6024 – 4398 = 1626, which, in engineering notation is 1.626×10^3. The difference between the two results is slight, amounting to only 0.06 %.

4. Divide: 6023.52 ÷ 4398.34

Retaining all the given digits, the quotient is 1.369498493. Rounding this off to four significant figures yields 1.369. However, if the two numbers are rounded off to four significant figures before the calculation, we get 6024 ÷ 4398 = 1.369713506, which, when rounded off to four significant figures, amounts to 1.370. In this case the two results differ by only 0.07 %.

5. Taking a square root: $\sqrt{6023.52}$

Retaining all the given digits: the square root is 77.61 to 4 significant figures.
Rounding off before taking the root: answer rounds off to 77.61, no appreciable difference.

6. Squaring a number: $6023.52^2 = 36.28 \times 10^6$

Rounding it off before squaring: this comes to 36.29×10^6
A difference of 0.03%

From the six examples above, it would appear that not much harm is done by rounding off numbers in a single-step calculation. However, at each successive stage of a calculation, if figures are rounded off, the effect is cumulative, and can lead to a much larger difference in the final answer.

This effect is particularly noticeable when one of the steps in a calculation involves using the result of a subtraction between two numbers that are very similar in magnitude. In such cases it makes a considerable difference if one rounds off.

For example, $4000 \div (45.5632 - 45.5207) = 94\,118$ or 94.12×10^3

If the numbers inside the bracket are rounded off to four significant figures before performing the calculation, the computation becomes $4000 \div (45.56 - 45.52)$ which equals $100\,000$ or 100.0×10^3, which differs from the correct value by almost 6%.

To avoid loss of accuracy when performing a calculation, it is best practice to retain all the digits resulting from the intermediate steps, and write only the final answer in engineering notation, reduced to four significant digits.

The units that apply to mechanical quantities in the S.I. system

In different countries, and at different times in history, people developed a large variety of different units for all the quantities that they needed to measure. Their definitions were arbitrary, and most of them had some kind of basis in the dimensions of the human body.

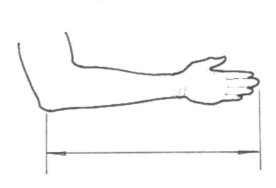

To give some indication of the colourful and complex historical evolution of units of measurement, and of the confusion that can arise from this chaos, we will focus on only one particular quantity, namely 'length'.

In the ancient Middle East, they used a unit of length called a cubit, defined as the length of a man's forearm, from the elbow to the tip of the outstretched middle finger. Naturally, not all men have the same dimensions, so a cubit, taken from such a definition, had to be standardised. Even so, there were different standardised 'short cubits' and 'long cubits' in use in the Hebrew, Egyptian and Babylonian cultures. These units ranged in length between about 44 and 52 cm.

A unit called the foot, or equivalent names to a foot, was used in many different countries, in different periods in history. Altogether we know of more than 70 different historical variations of the foot, which vary between about 250 mm and 350 mm.

In Roman times, they evolved a unit of length based on 1000 double paces (namely: left, right) marched by a soldier. Since the Latin word for 1000 is 'mille', this gave rise to the unit we know as the mile. However, the English mile is about 142 yards longer than the Roman mile.

In the English-speaking world, the traditional units of length, in use by the nineteenth century, were inches, feet, yards and miles. Furthermore, in these countries, many other units of length were also used, each developed for specific situations. For example, you may have heard of the chain, (22 yards) the furlong (220 yards), the league (3 miles), the fathom (6 feet) and the nautical mile (equal to one minute of longitude at the equator, taken as 2025 yards, or approximately 1.151 land miles).

In all countries, a huge variety of other units have been used, all developed locally and all different. When Europe was only a cluster of city-states, almost every one of them had its own unique unit of length measurement. The same degree of confusion applied in areas outside Europe. Besides having different units, there were often different versions of the official definition of any given unit. In China, for example, a unit of length called the 'li' was used, but the exact size of a li was redefined several times in successive dynasties.

Under circumstances like these, such a simple process as agreeing upon the length of an object became a complex and difficult task.

Within the last 200 years or so, scientists around the world began to become frustrated: it was inefficient to have to keep converting data from the units used in one country or region to those of another. Many people's efforts to standardise all units of measurement eventually resulted in the publication, in 1960, of the Système International d'Unités. This system is now abbreviated as SI, and uses, for all quantities, units that are standardised, based on multiples of ten, and linked to the units of other quantities. This system is in use in most countries in the world today.

Multiples of units in the S.I. system

In the SI system, there is a *basic unit* for each quantity. Multiples of the basic unit are indicated by prefixes. For example, the basic unit of length is the metre. Multiples of the metre include the *milli*metre and the *kilo*metre. The table that follows shows the commonest of these prefixes:

One trillionth (10^{-12}) of the basic unit	pico
One billionth (10^{-9}) of the basic unit	nano
One millionth (10^{-6}) of the basic unit	micro
One thousandth (10^{-3}) of the basic unit	milli
One hundredth (10^{-2}) of the basic unit	centi
One tenth (10^{-1}) of the basic unit	deci (pronounced *dessi*)
The unit itself	(no prefix)
Ten times the unit (10^1)	deca (pronounced *dekka*)
A hundred times the unit (10^2)	hecto
A thousand times the unit (10^3)	kilo
A million times the unit (10^6)	mega
A billion times the unit (10^9)	giga
A trillion times the unit (10^{12})	tera

The difference between precision and accuracy

The terms 'precision' and 'accuracy' in relation to numbers are often confused. However, these two terms have distinctly different meanings. A good way of illustrating the difference is by looking at the scatter of the bullet-holes in three targets, after 8 rounds have been fired into each, by three different competitors.

On target A, the shots are spread roughly around the bullseye. These shots are not accurate, because the objective of firing was to hit the bullseye, and this was not achieved. This competitor came close to that objective, but never quite accomplished it. The scatter of the shots shows inconsistency of method.

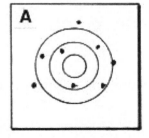 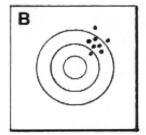 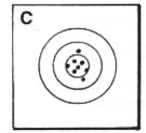

On target B, the shots are grouped very closely together. In every shot, almost the identical result was achieved. However, the group is some distance from the bullseye, so these shots also did not come close to the objective, and it is clear that they were not accurate.

From the closeness of the shots to one another, we can say this competitor fired with great consistency, and therefore with precision. There was something about the process of aiming and firing that was consistent. But the aiming was not accurate. Either the rifle sight needed adjusting, or the competitor made the same error on every shot.

On target C the shots were both accurate and precise.

From the above example we can see that 'accuracy' in a calculation means getting the right value, whereas 'precision' means a high degree of repeatability in a method.

Applying this distinction to making measurements in a laboratory: accurate measurements are those that truly reflect the value of the phenomenon being measured. Precise measurements are those that yield very close to the same value every time that a reading is repeated, whether or not that value is accurate. Ideally, measurements should be both precise and accurate.

Applying this distinction to calculations intended to solve problems: if you determine a number to ten decimal places, you have calculated with a great deal of precision. (Actually, it was your calculator, not you, that was responsible for this precision.) However, if your answer was not correct, then having determined it to ten decimal places was a waste of time. On the other hand, if you determine an answer to only three decimal places, and it matches very closely the correct answer, then your answer is more accurate, and hence more credible than the very precisely achieved, but inaccurate one.

Students often appear oblivious of this issue. They might, for example, round off the numbers achieved in the intermediate stages of a calculation, then use these rounded off numbers in a final calculation to produce an answer that they present, written down to ten decimal places, but which is of the order of 5% different from the true answer. The pretence of precision, in the circumstances, is meaningless.

The limitations of precision in a primarily practical science

For engineering purposes, there are *practical* limitations to relying on direct mathematical interpretations of mechanical laws.

Since the purpose of engineering is to make structures and devices that *work*, any numbers you come up with as a result of applying the principles of mechanics, have to fit in with reality. It is not productive to perform lengthy and complex calculations, only to find that the results are in conflict with other considerations that affect a design.

When to 'adjust' the results of calculations, with justification

Although it is good professional practice to apply principles mathematically wherever possible, sometimes we have to choose values that depart quite intentionally from the seeming precision of our calculated results.

We may have to do this for various reasons, which include:

- Deciding to make a machine part or a structural element stronger than the calculations showed was necessary, for safety reasons,
- Size or mass limitations on the machine or structure we are trying to design,
- Limitations on the availability and cost of raw materials,
- Limits on the options among ready-made parts at our disposal, for example, one may not be able to obtain standard gears with 53 teeth that mesh with others of 23 teeth, except at the great cost of having them custom-made,
- Manufacturing convenience, such as the impracticality of machining a pulley wheel whose diameter is accurate to within a micro-metre,
- Discovery of unintended effects when testing the machine or structure, and
- Our inability to make accurate allowance for 'nuisance' factors such as air resistance, due to the complex nature of such phenomena.

Nuisance factors that affect mechanical designs

No formula can possibly take account of everything that might affect a problem that has to be solved. When you apply a formula, you are effectively leaving out of the picture all the influencing factors *not* addressed by the formula.

There are *almost always* other 'nuisance' factors that do affect the picture. Among these could be, for example: friction, air resistance, local variations in values of the gravitational acceleration, deformation of materials under the action of forces, and the effects of temperature and pressure. Sometimes allowance also must be made to make parts fit with other parts whose form or function cannot be changed.

In addition, no arrangement of machinery obeys mechanical laws to the exclusion of all other laws. All the laws of chemistry and thermodynamics have to be obeyed too. Random occurrences, such as gusts of wind, consequences of corrosion, build-up of grit in lubricating fluids, expansion or contraction due to temperature changes, materials denaturing due to changes in temperature, and inherent flaws in materials, always stand a chance of getting in the way. The successful engineer is one who can think about the bigger picture and make allowances.

Here follow three examples of designers encountering nuisance factors too late, as experienced by this author.

The first was in the mining industry, when a company was asked to design a conveyor system that could run *underneath* the ore trolleys that carried blasted ore out of a mine tunnel. It was hoped that such a conveyor might supplement the ore removal capacity, to speed up the time between blasts.

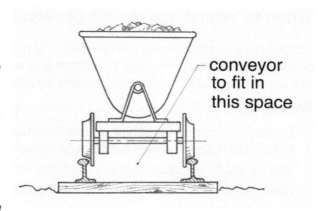

conveyor to fit in this space

They went ahead and built something which *appeared* viable on paper, but when they built it, the machine came to a grinding halt within three seconds of being switched on, as a result of grit blocking up the moving parts of the conveyor itself. When something like this happens, what can we say about slavish adherence to calculations?

The next two examples of unforeseen nuisance factors occurred to students of this author in the course of carrying out design-and-build projects.

One project required students to build a vehicle that would go as far as possible in a straight line on a flat floor in a given venue, powered by the energy given up by a 1 kg mass-piece descending a height of 0.5 m.

One team realised they needed to do everything in their power to reduce friction, so they decided to have the wooden axles running in ice-blocks. This seemed like a good idea, at first.

The machine started off alright, but within a few metres, the left ice-blocks started to wear away faster than the right ones, causing the vehicle to veer off to the left

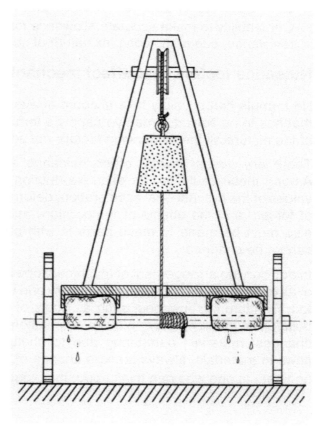

and crash against the barrier. This ruled them out of the contest. A hard lesson.

The second example occurred during a similar project, when students had designed a vehicle with axles made of wooden dowels running through holes drilled in the hardboard chassis, with minimum clearance. At the last minute the members of one team decided to lubricate the axles, so they applied some furniture oil to the bearing surfaces. They brought their vehicle to the starting line, released the mass-piece, and discovered that the vehicle would not move. The oil had swelled the wood of the axles, which jammed tight in the chassis holes.

It is wiser to have a broad understanding of such 'nuisance' factors, and have a feeling for the extent to which they influence our predictions, than to trust to simple equations learnt by rote, and hope that the answers they provide will reflect reality.

The constraints that affect the choice of a factor of safety in a mechanical design

Should we always make a part of a machine several times stronger than our calculations seem to indicate? We would be influenced in this decision by our need to account for what might possibly place our construction under the most extreme loading that we could imagine, given its location and type of use.

Frequently, we have to admit that the extreme loading conditions we imagine are pure estimates. We might also be unable to make *any* estimate for thermal stress or vibrational effects or corrosion, so that, to guard against the failure of the item we are designing, we might simply make an arbitrary choice to make the dimensions of the whole structure strong enough to withstand, say, twice the load our calculations projected. The factor of safety in such a case would be 2. However, we could just as easily have decided to make it three times as strong as our projected needs. In this case the factor of safety would have been 3.

It is clear that the choice of which factor of safety to use is arbitrary, to an extent. Certain contexts might require more caution than others, and so indicate the need to use a greater factor of safety.

However, if we are going to apply a factor of safety of any kind, then one may well ask what the use is of calculating results to a high degree of accuracy in the first place. The answer to this question is that the use of a factor of safety does not invalidate appropriate calculations. Such calculations are necessary to determine the *minimum* requirements of our design.

A 'factor of safety' is sometimes disparagingly referred to as a 'factor of ignorance'. There is truth in that: indeed, we just have to face up to it, we cannot know everything about the performance of a device before we put it to the test.

However, as an engineer, your reputation will suffer immeasurably if something that you have designed fails with deleterious effects to life and property. It is therefore completely sensible to make use of a factor of safety, in an attempt to achieve the best outcomes for all concerned.

It is true that there are some situations in which it is necessary to pare down the mass or the costs as much as possible, and therefore to be cautious of using an over-generous factor of safety. In such situations, there is no substitute for experience.

This author, when a student, had the privilege of attending classes given by a lecturer from eastern Europe, who, as a young engineer at the time of WW2, was commandeered by the Nazis to design steam engines for their war effort. The surreptitious form of resistance he embarked upon was to design the engine parts so close to the limits of endurance, that they would pass all inspections, but mysteriously fail in service, very soon after being commissioned. He knew all about factors of safety.

A perspective on the value of calculations

Those who are inclined to set great store by precise number-crunching should always keep in perspective this fact: it is possible to design machines and products that work very well, *without performing a single calculation.*

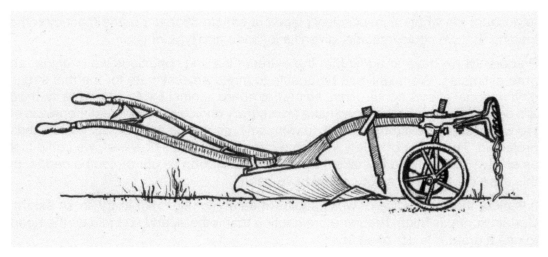

How else could people of thousands of years ago have started to design ploughs, chariots and potters' wheels?

The essential process of engineering has always been, and is still this:

You get an idea that something might work, you build it, you discover where it needs improving, and by trial and error, you converge on a better design.

Even in today's world, despite most academic courses in engineering giving the impression that calculations are the backbone of your studies, there is a lot of engineering that takes place quite successfully, based on hunches, intuition, broad estimations based on experience, and trial and error.

The numbers which our calculations produce are only a starting point for further responsible decision-making.

Converting the units of quantities, e.g. kilometres to miles

If all engineers used only the S.I. system of units, there would be little cause to convert the values of quantities from one system of units to another, such as gallons to litres. However, many products are manufactured in units other than S.I. units, either because a different system is still used in the country of manufacture, or because the 'new' size is a direct conversion from what worked before, when that country was using its previous system.

For example, hardware stores in a number of English-speaking countries supply dressed (planed) wood in a thickness of 19 mm, (sometimes 18 mm) which dimensions correspond closely to ¾ inch. That is an odd number in mm, so why did they not decide to supply wood that is 20 mm thick? Two reasons: a thickness of 19 mm is a really convenient size for general wood-working, and tradition dies hard.

Calculators have programmes for converting units that will list the direct equivalents, say from inches to millimetres. Using such tables is straightforward. However, often one needs to convert a quantity from one complex unit to another. Even though you may find conversion tables for some of these on the internet, you still need to know the procedure, so that you can check any value you have looked up, and in case you have to do a conversion for which you cannot find a table or a programme.

Converting complex units

A complex unit is one that consists of multiples of other units, such as $kg.m^2$, or a unit divided by other units, such as km/h.

There is an easy, reliable procedure to perform these conversions. We'll demonstrate firstly with a very simple example: Convert 80 miles per hour to metres per second, given that 1 mile = 1.6093 km

1. Write down the given quantity together with its units, and set this equal to itself.

80 miles/hour = 80 miles/hour

This may look trivial, but we are going to start with this statement and set up an equation. Up to this point, the statement of the equation is valid, and we want to keep it that way.

2. Now multiply the quantity to the right of the equals sign by a series of factors, each of which is chosen to equal *unity*.

The equation will only remain true if the value of the r.h.s. does *not* change. The only factors we can multiply the r.h.s. with, that will not change its value, are factors that are each equal to 1.

We choose appropriate factors according to the units we want to end up with. If we choose factors with units as follows, and multiply them all out, cancelling units as if they were numerical factors, we will obtain the desired units, namely m/s.

$$\frac{\text{miles}}{\text{hour}} = \frac{\text{miles}}{\text{hour}} \times \frac{\text{hours}}{\text{second}} \times \frac{\text{metres}}{\text{mile}}$$

In setting up each factor, note that it represents the value 1 if the numerator is identical to the denominator.

Since 1 hour is equivalent to 3600 seconds, the factor: $\dfrac{1\ \text{hour}}{3600\ \text{seconds}}$ is equal to 1.

Now, 1.6093 km = 1 mile, so the factor $\dfrac{1609.3\ \text{m}}{1\ \text{mile}}$ also represents the value 1.

The equation now looks as follows:

$$80\ \text{miles/hour} = \frac{80\ \text{miles}}{1\ \text{hour}} \times \frac{1\ \text{hour}}{3600\ \text{seconds}} \times \frac{1609.3\ \text{m}}{\text{mile}}$$

3. Now multiply out the terms on the r.h.s. of the equation, taking care to cancel units where possible.

This means that if we find a unit on the top line (numerator) in any factor, we can cancel that unit with *the same* unit anywhere on the bottom line (denominator). In this way we can eliminate the units that are no longer required, leaving only the units in which the answer needs to be expressed. Hence:

$$80\ \text{miles/hour} = \frac{80\ \cancel{\text{miles}}}{1\ \cancel{\text{hour}}} \times \frac{1\ \cancel{\text{hour}}}{3600\ \text{seconds}} \times \frac{1609.3\ \text{m}}{\cancel{\text{mile}}} = 128.7\ \text{m/s}$$

Example

How many square metres are there in a piece of ground with an area of 25 acres?

Given that:

1 inch = 25.40 mm exactly; 1 m = 1000 mm; 12 inches = 1 foot; 3 feet = 1 yard; 1 acre = 4840 square yards (easy to remember: an acre is an area equivalent to a rectangle with dimensions one chain by one furlong, namely 22 by 220 yards = 4840 square yards).

Method: First, the equation: 25 acres = 25 acres × some factors, each equal to 1. We need to end up with a value with units of m² and no other remaining units, either on the top line or the bottom line. So, we choose factors with units as follows:

$$\frac{25\ \text{acres}}{1} \times \frac{\text{yd}^2}{\text{acre}} \times \frac{\text{mm}}{\text{ft}} \times \frac{\text{mm}}{\text{ft}} \times \frac{\text{m}}{\text{mm}} \times \frac{\text{m}}{\text{mm}} \times \frac{\text{ft}}{\text{yd}} \times \frac{\text{ft}}{\text{yd}}$$

giving a result in units of m², as follows: 25 acres =

$$\frac{25\ \text{acres}}{1} \times \frac{4840\ \text{yd}^2}{1\ \text{acre}} \times \frac{(12 \times 25.4)\ \text{mm}}{1\ \text{ft}} \times \frac{(12 \times 25.4)\ \text{mm}}{1\ \text{ft}} \times \frac{1\ \text{m}}{10^3\ \text{mm}} \times \frac{1\ \text{m}}{10^3\ \text{mm}} \times \frac{3\ \text{ft}}{\text{yd}} \times \frac{3\text{ft}}{\text{yd}}$$

= 101171.4 m², which depending on your purpose, might or might not need to be rounded off and expressed in engineering notation. If you needed an approximate answer, you could say this is roughly 101.2×10^3 m², but if you were buying the land and needed the exact amount to be shown on the title deeds, you would stick with the full answer obtained.

Exercises on converting units

The exercises that follow should be done using only the conversion data supplied in this chapter, without referring to conversion tables, or using a programmed device.

1. A refrigerator is claimed to have a useable interior volume of 5.6 cubic feet. How many litres is this?   [158.6 l]

2. Convert a volume of 582 barrels to cubic metres, given that one barrel contains 42 US gallons, and one US gallon = 3.7854 litres   [92.53 m³]

3. A car in the UK is claimed to have a fuel consumption of 45 miles per gallon. What is the equivalent in km/litre? 1 gallon (UK) = 4.5461 litres [15.93 km/l]

4. A meteorite dug out of a crater is roughly rectangular, approximately 8 ft × 3 ft × 4 ft and weighs 21.8 imperial tons. Determine its approximate density, in kg/m³, given: 1 kg = 2.2046 lb. and 1 Imperial ton = 2240 lb. [8148 kg/m³]

5. Rain falls steadily for two hours and thirty-five minutes on a farm occupying 91.86 Ha. The farmer measures the fall at 42 mm. On average, how many cubic feet of rain per second fell on his farm during this period?   [146.5 ft³/s]

6. A rifle bullet travels at 700 m/s. What is this speed in miles per hour? [1566 mph]

Units Preferred by Engineers

For the manufacture of machinery and all parts of machinery, engineering drawings, by convention, are always given in mm, unless specified otherwise. If you look at a drawing and see no units given to accompany the dimensions shown on the drawing, those dimensions will refer to mm. i.e. '384' implies '384 mm'.

In some circumstances, with larger equipment or building plans, the dimensions will be given in metres, but in such cases, they will always be designated specifically as metres.

Engineers seldom use centimetres, although they should be conversant with centimetres, as the centimetre is the unit preferred by lay people in describing the dimensions of furniture and clothing.

Some engineers express a preference for using diameters in equations, rather than radii. This preference comes from the fact that it is much easier to measure the diameter of a finished product than it is to measure its radius.

However, if you consider the fact that it is impossible to make an object that has a diameter unless a radius has been used in drawing it or for turning the object on a lathe, then it is clear that a radius is every bit as important as a diameter. This author prefers to use radii in equations, as the form of an equation containing a radius is frequently a lot simpler than it would be if a diameter were used.

For example, the area of a circle can be expressed either as πr^2 or $\pi D^2/4$. The shorter and simpler form is easier to remember, and the use of it is less likely to lead to making mistakes in calculations.

Conclusion

In this chapter we have covered the basic conventions for the use of numbers, and shown a perspective on the accuracy required in engineering calculations.

The treatment given in this chapter is by no means exhaustive. There are other aspects to the use of numbers that will be encountered in your studies: aspects such as statistics and error analysis, that apply to laboratory practice. These are not dealt with here.

However, if you grasped the ideas put forward here, you are ready to go ahead and attempt solutions to mechanics exercises that involve calculations.

The chapter that follows deals with that most basic and essential aspect of mechanics: how to analyse forces.

Chapter 4

Forces

- *The nature and origins of forces*
- *Mass, weight and gravitation*
- *Scalars and vectors*
- *Vector addition of forces: resultants and equilibrants*
- *Components of a force: general and rectangular components*
- *Determining a resultant by summation of rectangular components*
- *The principle of transmissibility of a force*
- *Equilibrium conditions for a particle in 2-D*

The nature and origins of forces

What is a force?

It is difficult to define a force, because forces are not visible. You can only see or feel their effect. When a crane lifts a heavy container into the air, you understand that it must be exerting a force in order to overcome the gravitational force that the earth exerts on the container. However, you can't see the force itself.

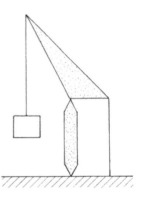

The different effects that forces can have

Forces acting on solid objects can have any combination of the following visible effects:

They can

resist other forces;   move an object;   rotate an object;   or deform an object.

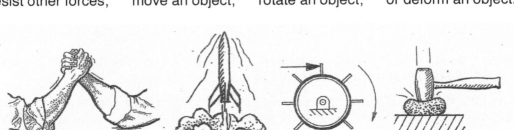

If any one of these effects is observed, one can deduce that a force must be acting.

It is impossible for any agent, human or otherwise, to just 'exert' a force, without having something to exert it on. Just try, for example, to push your arms sideways with a force of 200 N when there is nothing to push against. It is impossible. You may have the *capability* of exerting that amount of force, but unless there is some resistance there to oppose your effort, the actual force you are exerting is limited to that needed to push the air out of the way of your arms. So, a force cannot exist on its own, without pushing or pulling against some resistance.

This fact is so important that it gives rise to what this author calls **The zeroth law of mechanics**: *a force cannot even exist unless it is opposed*. This statement needs to be grasped before we can fully appreciate the meaning of Newton's third Law.

Since a force can only exist if it is opposed, all forces occur in opposing pairs.

- If you support a load while standing on the ground, you can only push upwards if you exert an equal and opposite force downwards on the ground.

- If you squash a grape between your finger and thumb, your finger and your thumb have to exert equal and opposite forces.

- In order to accelerate a children's roundabout, you have to push against the ground in such a way that part of your effort is directed parallel to the ground. The horizontal force you exert on the roundabout is equal and opposite to the horizontal force you exert on the ground.

- The force that compresses a spring must be matched by the force with which the spring resists that force.

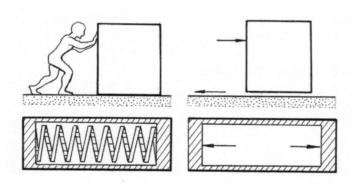

Whenever we consider a force acting on an object of interest, we need to keep in mind that the force we are focusing on is only one half of an opposing pair of equal forces.

The other half could either be acting on the surroundings, or acting on another part of the object of interest, as shown here.

Even if we are not interested in the other half of a force pair, it is there, somewhere, or else the half that we *are* interested in would not exist.

The next diagram shows the pairs of points at which equal and opposite forces must exist, for a crane supporting a load. The force at point A will be equal and opposite to the force at point B, and so on.

Point 'M' is the centre of mass of the load, and point 'N' represents the Earth. There is a pair of equal and opposite gravitational forces between points M and N.

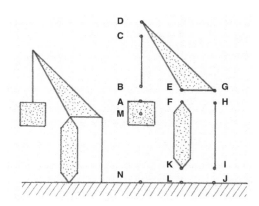

For visual simplicity, the diagram does not show the centres of mass of the parts of the crane, to illustrate the gravitational attraction between each part and the Earth, although they should ideally be included, for completeness.

Newton's 3rd Law states: whenever two objects are in contact, they exert equal and opposite forces on one another. True. However, while the *magnitudes* of those opposing forces are equal, the *effects* of those forces on the respective objects might be vastly different.

For example, consider what happens when a tennis racquet strikes a tennis ball at high speed. The forces that the racquet and ball exert on each other are equal in magnitude at all times while they are in contact, but the *effects* that those forces have on the respective objects differ, on account of their respective masses. The force between racquet and ball is sufficient to accelerate the ball rapidly, but the same magnitude of force will not disturb the momentum of the heavier racquet (combined with the player's arm and body movement) to a significant extent.

Be wary of the expression that is commonly used to summarise Newton's 3rd law, namely that 'action = reaction'. This mantra is misleading, as it seems to indicate that the *effects* of the two opposing forces are equal, which is hardly ever the case. It is best to avoid using that expression entirely.

The various causes that give rise to forces

Muscular action

From experience, we know that a force can be exerted by either pushing or pulling. For example, in the sport of weight-lifting, you *pull* the bar upwards off the ground, and *push* it upwards above your head. The *cause* of these particular forces is muscular contraction, which is the commonest source of force available to people.

Humans exert force by contracting and relaxing specific muscles. We do this all day long, when walking, lifting weights, steering a car, typing on a keyboard, or stirring a pot. Muscular action allows us to crank a winch, haul on a rope, or raise a weight. For most of humankind's long history, the only source of force available to us, for engineering purposes, was muscular action, either by humans or animals.

Every product of civilisation was originally made entirely by hand, including shaped masonry, fired bricks, slate roof tiles, wooden furniture, musical instruments, woven cloth, coins, wagons, barrels and scissors, just to name a few. One should not think that just because we now have access to greater forces than those our own muscles can exert, that we should dismiss muscular force as irrelevant. Our standard of appreciation of most physical phenomena, like height, speed and force, is based on comparisons with the dimensions and capabilities of our own bodies.

If you want to appreciate the magnitude of the force units in engineering usage, you should get to know how much force you can exert using your muscles directly. Can you raise from the ground a load weighing 100 N? What about 300 N? Or 500 N? You really ought to find this out from practical experience, because, as an engineer, you can only understand force magnitudes that apply to machinery, by knowing what you can do with your own muscles. It is not sufficient to *talk about the numerical value of a newton*: you need to *feel* the magnitude of a newton.

For this purpose, it is a useful exercise to pull in opposite directions the ends of a spring-scale, and read off the scale how much force you are exerting. Typical university students in the author's classes have been capable of exerting a pulling force ranging from 125 to 500 N.

There are strong men out there who can make pulling 500 N look like nothing. And of course, it is impressive to see the feats of strength demonstrated by competitors in competitions like 'World's Strongest Man'. People who take part in such competitions are specialists, and their genetics and training makes them far stronger than most of us.

The average person of today is much less physically strong than people needed to be in earlier times.

For example, the average trained and fit archer of today draws a bow requiring a pull of 40 to 50 pounds, for which the S.I. equivalent is approximately 200 to 260 N.

On exhibit in the Cultural History Museum in Vienna is a bow used by a Turkish cavalryman in the assault on that city in 1529. This bow requires a pull of some 150 pounds, or 670 N. Most archers of today could not even pull that once, let alone all day long, in battle.

Although the average person of today is not as strong as people were in ancient times, we still need our muscles, and very little would be accomplished without them.

Muscles are here to stay, and should never be neglected as a source of force for the engineer. However, as we will see shortly, muscular force is only one of about a dozen sources of force available to us.

Why are forces important?

Much of mechanical engineering is about using and transforming either forces, or energy, to get an effect we want. Some examples:

- An earth-digger transforms the energy stored in diesel fuel to a force that drives the digging bucket to move soil.
- An air-conditioner uses electrical energy to regulate the temperature and humidity of air.
- A bicycle transforms muscular energy into a forward propulsion force.
- A welding machine converts electrical energy to heat, to melt metal.

Any device that transforms a force or adapts energy from one form to another, for a particular purpose, is called a machine. A machine can be as simple as a bottle-opener, or as complex as a space-station. No machine is an end in itself. It is built to accomplish a purpose. If we could use our mental concentration to melt metal, we wouldn't need a welding machine. But, until we reach that exalted state, we have to be content to use machines to accomplish such purposes.

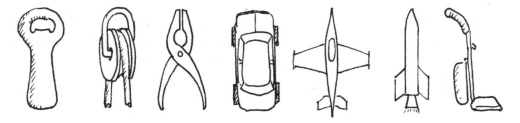

Forces are responsible for movement. Without movement, and hence, without forces, life could not exist. Without forces, the blood in your arteries could not move. Air could not get into your lungs, and you would not be able to bite or chew. You couldn't sustain life. No creature could.

Most machines make use of forces, either as part of the process of their operation (for example, transmitting forces by means of gears, levers and hydraulic cylinders), or in their end result (for example, to accelerate the occupants of a vehicle).

Some machines have forces as their input and output (the bicycle) and some principally as their output (the jack-hammer).

To manufacture a product, or a machine, or even any part of a machine, requires the application of forces. Almost all manufacturing processes make use of forces. Such processes include hammering, drilling, forming, sawing, bending, and punching of holes. The only processes that are exceptions to this are those that make exclusive use of heat or chemical reactions.

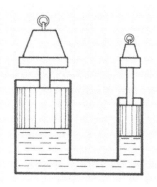

Different sources of force available to the engineer
(in no particular order)

- **Muscular contraction:** humans or animals performing work.
- **Expansion and contraction of solids, liquids or gases**, due to temperature changes. (As in steam engines and Stirling engines.)
- **Expansion or contraction of gases** due to a chemical reaction. (As in combustion engines, ammunition and rocket motors.)
- **Gravity** causes objects possessing mass to be attracted to one another with a force. Objects or fluids descending within a gravitational field can exert forces. The rise and fall of ocean tides is also caused by gravity, and this movement of water can, in turn, give rise to forces.
- **The motion of the waves in the sea** (as distinct from the rise and fall of tides) can exert forces.
- **Inertial forces:** objects in motion tend to keep moving, for example, a rotating wheel tends to continue rotating and will exert a force on its surroundings when an attempt is made to stop it.
- **Buoyancy** causes there to be an upward force on a solid object in a liquid or gaseous medium.
- **Compressed or extended springs** can exert a force.
- **Magnets and electro-magnets** exert forces.
- **A jet of liquid** (for example, water from a hosepipe) **or gas** (say, the wind) exerts a force against objects placed in its path. Water in a flowing river can drive a waterwheel or a turbine.
- **A stream of photons** from a light source exerts a force (very small, but measurable).
- **An electric current** passing through a conductor in a magnetic field causes the conductor to experience a force. (The phenomenon that makes electric motors operate.)

If ever you need an original approach when designing something mechanical, it may be helpful to use the above list as a checklist, to make sure you have not neglected any possibilities for the primary source of force.

Making the connection between forces, energy sources, and desired effects

See if you can complete the table opposite:

Process	Source of energy or force	Desired effect
Pedalling a bicycle	Muscular contraction	Forward propulsion
Pressing a lift button	The triggering force is muscular contraction, and the force accomplishing the task comes from an electric motor.	Upward/downward movement of the lift
Firing a retro-rocket on a space-ship	Chemical energy in fuel	Deceleration
Pile-driver falling onto a pile	Gravity	Pile penetrates the ground
Operating a clockwork toy car		
Shooting an arrow from a bow		
Running a petrol-driven lawnmower		
Firing an air-gun		
Firing a cannon		
Operating a hydraulic jack		
Making a hot air balloon ascend		

Force measurement exercises

Try out the force-measuring equipment you have at your disposal, to *identify the approximate magnitude*, in newtons, of each of the following forces.

Force	Magnitude of this force, measured in [N]
The horizontal force that an adult can exert by pulling a rope attached to a wall, while standing with both feet on a level floor.	
The maximum weight that you can lift off the ground without straining your back.	
The buoyancy of a soccer ball in water. Measure the force required to keep the ball just submerged.	

The force required to push a car on a level surfaced road, with a driver in the seat, the brakes off, and the car in neutral gear.	
The weight of one standard building brick.	
The force required (when applied slowly) to turn the crank handle of a scissors jack, when lifting the side of a small car to change a wheel.	
The weight of a rectangular wooden beam provided, whose dimensions you can also measure.	

Force estimation exercise *(suitable for solving in a small group)*

Without making any measurements except those made above, discuss in your group, and perform appropriate calculations to estimate the approximate magnitude, in newtons, of each of the following forces. Do not cheat by looking up figures or by making further measurements. The idea of this exercise is to develop your ability to comprehend the magnitude of the force unit called the newton, through personal experience.

1. The weight of a wooden dining room table (6-seater) , made from the same kind of wood as the beam you previously weighed.

2. The buoyancy force on a light nylon net containing ten beach balls, held under the surface of a body of water. Assume each ball has a diameter that is one and a half times the diameter of a soccer ball.

3. The weight of a tree-trunk that is 7 m long, has an average circumference of 1.4 m, and density the same as that of the beam you used in the previous exercise.

4. How many men would be needed to lift this tree trunk?

5. The weight of the amount of water typically let into a bath for one person's use.

6. The outward force on a piece of motor car tyre wall that is 40 mm × 40 mm, when the pressure inside the tyre is 2 bars greater than the pressure outside the tyre.

7. The weight of a brick wall that is 6 m long, 3m high and 250 mm thick. Assume that the density of the mortar is no different from that of brick.

8. The wind force on a triangular sail of height 4m and base 2.5m, if a man can only just remain on his feet while holding a piece of similar sail in a square frame, 0.5m by 0.5m, perpendicular to the wind.

9. The force in the rope in a tug-o-war with ten people in each team. What should be the load rating of the rope you use?

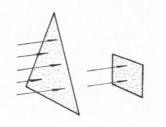

Mass, weight, and gravitation

The definition of mass

Mass is commonly defined in two different ways, neither of which lead to a reliable, convenient way of measuring mass.

Firstly, the mass of an object is sometimes described as a measure of *how much matter* is contained in that object. This definition is easy to understand, but virtually impossible to confirm by measurement. The concept of matter is itself completely general and cannot be defined, except in the vaguest manner, relying on our intuition of 'how much stuff' something might comprise. Even if you thought the idea of 'matter' could be brought into focus by counting atoms: you can't count atoms, so you can never know exactly how many atoms of which atomic weight there are in an object. So, this definition of mass cannot be used to measure mass.

Secondly, mass has also been described as *that which is responsible for inertia*, namely the property of an object that resists changes to its motion. The more mass in an object, the harder it is to accelerate or decelerate the object. We know this from adding passengers to a car and seeing the resulting sluggishness when attempting to accelerate the car.

This phenomenon is described by Newton's 2nd Law, which states that $F = ma$.

However, it is very complicated to try to measure mass by the amount of inertia that an object manifests. The complication comes from the necessity of measuring the *force* acting on an object, at the same time as measuring the *acceleration* that results. Also, if we conduct such a measurement in air, the measurements are complicated by the fact that air resistance varies with the velocity of the object. So, this particular definition of mass also does not provide us with a convenient way to measure mass.

How mass is *actually* measured

The only reliable and convenient method of determining the value of a mass is to *weigh* it. We put it on a weighing scale, which gives an indication of the force with which gravity attracts the object towards the earth.

If the scale shows *the same reading* as would be shown by a standard mass of 100 kg, then we assume that the mass of our object is also 100 kg.

For thousands of years, mass was measured using a set of balances, which compared the weight of an object directly with the weight of a standard mass-piece. Such balances, though reliable, take time to adjust, and occupy a fair amount of space, so they have been largely superseded by other types of weighing scales that give direct readings, such as electronic scales and the spring scales used in laboratories.

It is common usage in the general population to speak of the *weight* of an object in terms of kilograms. While this practice is convenient, it is not scientifically correct. We need to keep in perspective the difference between mass and weight. A weighing scale that gives a direct reading measures *weight*, not mass. Suppose you put a bucket of sand on your bathroom scale at home, and it reads 26.0 kg. If you put the same bucket on the same scale, at the top of a high mountain, where the gravitational force is diminished, the scale would yield a *different* reading, measurably less than 26 kg. To understand this, we need to understand the connection between weight and gravity.

Weight, Newton's Law of Gravitation, and gravitational acceleration

Isaac Newton, following the work of Robert Hooke, confirmed that a gravitational force exists between any two objects in the universe. Simply due to the fact that the objects have mass, they attract each other. This means that if two rocks are drifting in space, near one another, they will each exert a pull on the other, the result of which is that they will gradually accelerate towards one another. The more mass the two objects possess, the greater is this force. The further apart they are, the smaller is this force. Newton's Law of Gravitation tell us that the magnitude of the gravitational force, F, depends on these variables, in the following relationship:

$F = (Gm_1m_2)/r^2$

Where G is the universal gravitation constant, m_1 and m_2 are the masses of the two objects, and r is the distance between their centres of gravity.

This law applies to *all* bodies, not only to the gravitational force between a given object and the Earth. Every object that possesses mass attracts every other object with a force of attraction given by the above equation. It might be hard to believe that two pencils lying on your desk exert a gravitational pull on one another, but they do. The magnitude of this pull is insignificant, because both of their masses are vastly smaller than the mass of the earth.

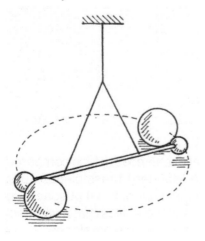

The magnitude of the gravitational force of attraction between two small objects was first determined in a famous experiment by the British scientist Henry Cavendish in 1797.

A torsion wire suspended from an overhead beam supported a horizontal rod, on the ends of which were mounted two small lead spheres.

When the rod had settled into an equilibrium position, two larger spheres were brought from a distance, to a position on the circle of movement close to the small ones, and equidistant from them. The small spheres moved towards the larger ones with a force that could be determined by the amount of twist they caused in the torsion wire.

What we know as the *weight* of an object is the gravitational force between that object and the Earth. It is the force that the Earth exerts on the object, and is directed from the centre of gravity of the object towards the centre of gravity of the Earth. Your exact weight depends on the distance, r, that you are located from the centre of the Earth. The further you are from the centre of the Earth, the less you weigh.

The accepted value of G, the universal gravitation constant which appears in Newton's equation, has been established by scientists to be 6.693×10^{-11} N(m/kg)^2. This value was determined with the greatest accuracy to date, in 2007. Prior to that, a slightly different value was in use.

When using this value of G in Newton's equation, with the units stated above, masses should be stated in kg and distances in metres. Scientists have established that the radius of the Earth averages 6378100 m. An average has to be used, because the Earth is not perfectly spherical. They have also determined that the mass of the Earth is 5.9742×10^{24} kilograms.

If we use these values to determine the weight of an 80 kg man at sea level:

The weight force, $F = (Gm_1m_2)/r^2 = (6.693 \times 10^{-11} \times 5.9742 \times 10^{24} \times 80) \div (6378100)^2$
$$= 786.3 \text{ N}$$

To check this result: we are always told (quite appropriately) that weight = mg, where g is the value of the gravitational acceleration, generally taken to have a standard value of 9.81 m/s^2. Using the standard value for g, we see that the man in our example weighs $80 \times 9.81 = 784.8$ N. This value differs from the first value by 0.19%. Does that mean our value for g (or for G) might be inaccurate?

Scientists have declared the standard value of g at sea level to be *exactly* 9.80665 m/s^2. It is common practice, for nearly all engineering purposes, to round this off to 9.81 m/s^2, which value is acceptable for most general calculations in engineering. However, it is not as simple as that. The local value of g actually *differs* slightly at different places around the world, varying from roughly 9.76 m/s^2 to 9.83 m/s^2, according to the exact radius of the Earth at the given position, the height above sea level and the local distribution of mass deep in the Earth, directly below the particular place.

We simply have to accept that, given the variation in g values, and the variation in the exact distance from the centre to the surface of the Earth from place to place, that the weight equivalents in newtons of given masses in kilograms, determined by calculating using W = mg, could be uncertain by as much as approximately 0.2%.

Now, supposing the 80 kg man in our example were flying in a spacecraft at a height of 20 km above sea level. By how much would his weight change?

We would use Newton's equation of universal gravitation to find his *new* weight, noting that the distance between the man and the centre of the Earth has now increased.

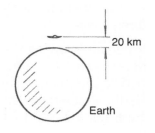

The value for r, the distance between the man and the centre of the Earth, would now be (6378100 + 20000) m. This results in the value F = 781.4 N. So, his weight would have reduced from 786.3 N to 781.4 N, namely by nearly 5 N, which is about the weight of a 500 gram block of butter, and is therefore hardly noticeable to the astronaut. However, once you start moving further out into space, and the distance r increases significantly, your weight reduces very significantly.

Some computations to try:

1. If your mass is 60 kg, as indicated by a bathroom scale at sea level, what would the same bathroom scale indicate if you used it to weigh yourself at the top of a high mountain, 8000 m above sea level? Assume your mass did not diminish from one weighing to the next. [59.85 kg]

2. If you weigh 700 N at the surface on the Earth, what will be your weight when you are half of the Earth's radius above the surface? [311.1 N]

3. If you weigh 700 N at the surface of the earth, how much will you weigh at the surface of a planet that has twice the mass of the Earth, and the same average density? [881.9 N]

Here's a tricky one: Using the equation given by Newton's law of gravitation, what will be your weight when you are halfway between the surface and the centre of the Earth? (Ignoring the impossibility of surviving at the temperature that prevails there.)

If we apply Newton's equation, it would appear that your weight would increase to four times its usual value!

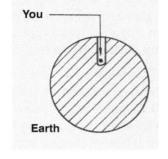

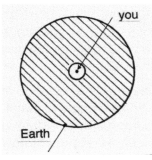

The result of such a calculation would be even more alarming, if you applied the Universal Law of Gravitation to determine your weight when you are situated in a hypothetical hole right in the centre of the Earth.

According to Newton's equation, if r = 0, your weight would be infinite. Could this really be the case? Definitely not.

Once an object goes *inside* the Earth, the gravitational pull of some of the Earth's mass *above* the object will be counteracting the pull of the rest of the Earth's mass that is still *below* it.

In fact, if you were able to sit in a hole exactly at the centre of the earth, the gravitational pull of the mass all around you would be completely even in all directions, and you would experience zero gravity.

In case you are wondering if you would be pulled apart by the surrounding gravitational field, you wouldn't, since every particle of your body would experience the same pull from all the mass particles that lay in every direction around you. These forces would be neutralised, so there would be no force trying to separate your constituent particles.

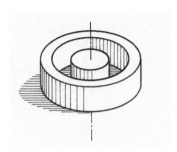

Another demonstration of the inapplicability of Newton's Law of Gravitation to a case where one object is physically inside the other: Suppose you place a small metal cylinder exactly in the centre of a metal ring, so that their centres of mass coincide. Applying Newton's equation, r = 0, therefore the gravitational force between the two objects ought to be infinite, so you should not be able to separate them. But we know it is no trouble to move them apart, so the equation cannot apply in such a circumstance.

We have to conclude that Newton's equation does not apply when one object is physically inside the outer boundary of the other. When an object is situated inside the Earth, the gravitational force on it would seem to vary from whatever value it has at the surface, to zero at the centre, by a progression that is most probably not linear.

However, considering the impossibility of getting to the centre of the Earth, we are unlikely ever to be able to test this reasoning to the full. We could *partially* test the reasoning, by weighing an object on the surface of the Earth, and then using the same weighing scale to weigh the same object as far underground as we are able to place it. At the time of writing, the deepest mine in the world goes down only 3.9 km. This puts a very practical limitation on our ability to carry out such a test.

If there is one thing we learn from the discussion above, it is that it is unsound engineering practice to place our faith in an equation that purports to be universally valid. It is always necessary to examine the limitations of an equation, by applying common sense.

Exercises on mass and weight

1. Can the amount of matter in an object be determined directly?

2. How is a bathroom scale able to give you a reading of your 'mass'? Does it measure mass directly? Explain.

3. Builders talk about a bag of cement 'weighing' 50 kg. Identify which of the following statements are scientifically correct:

a. The kg is a unit of weight.

b. The mass of a bag of cement is 50 kg.

c. The force with which the earth attracts a bag of cement is 50 kg.

d. A bag of cement affects a weighing scale in the same way that a standard mass of 50 kg would.

e. A bag of cement attracts the Earth towards it with a force of (50 × 9.81) newtons.

f. The Earth attracts a bag of cement towards it with a force of (50 × 9.81) newtons.

4. If you place two similar hard metal spheres some distance apart on a perfectly flat, hard-surfaced horizontal table, would they move towards each other, or away from each other, or remain where they are? Explain.

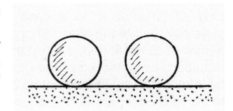

5. From reference sources, find out and write down the equivalent in kg or grams of each of the following units of mass:

a. One pound (lb.)..

b. One carat (a unit used for weighing diamonds)................................

c. One grain (a unit used for weighing precious metals)........................

d. One stone (a unit used in England for weighing people).....................

6. What is the mass of an average building brick or block, as used in the region where you live?

7. Approximately how many such bricks/blocks make up one tonne?

Scalars and Vectors

The differences between scalars and vectors

Any phenomenon such as length, weight, and time, that can be measured, is referred to as a 'quantity'. A quantity can be either a scalar or a vector.

Scalars: These are quantities that can be measured on some single scale of magnitude. For example: mass, length, volume, density, elasticity, and temperature.

Vectors: These are all quantities that need to be specified in terms of *both* magnitude *and* direction, in order to be properly defined. For example: displacement, velocity, acceleration, force, and stress.

Suppose you are told about a force with a magnitude of 86 N. This number alone cannot completely define the force, because a downward force of 86 N is very different from a sideways or an upward force of the same value.

Likewise, a displacement of 24 m to the left of a reference point is completely different from a displacement of 24 m to the right of that point. Any given vector acts in a specific direction, which has to be specified, in order to define the vector.

All vectors can be indicated *graphically* by drawing an arrow showing the direction in which they have an effect. The magnitude of the vector is indicated by the length of the arrow, drawn to some chosen scale.

Adding scalars

In cases where it is meaningful to add scalars, they can be added arithmetically, because they don't have different effects in different directions. If a bucket contains 3 kg of sand, and you add another 4kg of sand, you have altogether 7 kg of sand. While certain scalars can be added, it does not make sense to add all types of scalar: for instance, there is no point in adding two densities.

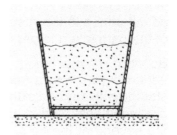

Adding vectors

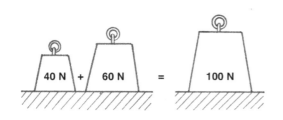

If two vectors *happen to be orientated in the same direction*, it is easy to see that the effect of the two acting together must be the same as the arithmetic sum of their values.

If the vectors are directly opposed, then adding them amounts to determining the arithmetic difference between their values.

However, if two vectors are *not* acting in the same line of action, and we want to determine their combined effect (namely, their resultant), we cannot simply add their values. Their combined effect depends very much on their direction.

Vector addition for co-planar vectors not in the same straight line

We will demonstrate the principle behind vector addition, using displacements, which are also vectors. The same principle will apply to the addition of other vectors, including forces, velocities and accelerations.

A displacement vector defines *where* an object is in relation to a given point of reference. To define a displacement, you have to specify *both* a distance and a direction.

Suppose we are in a city in which the streets are arranged in a rectangular grid, and we need to specify the displacement of point K from point J.

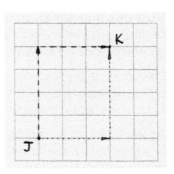

To travel from point J to point K, there are many possible options. One of the simplest options is to go north for 4 blocks, then east for 3 blocks.

Or, alternatively, one could start by travelling 3 blocks to the east, and from there, go 4 blocks north. Either way, you end up in the same place.

Even if you took a zig-zag path, or a route that back-tracked upon itself, you would end up with the correct displacement of point K, by combining a total displacement of 4 blocks north with one of 3 blocks east. The order in which this is done makes no difference to the result. The displacement of K from J is the same, irrespective of the path taken to get there.

So, two displacement vectors are added by drawing a vector diagram, starting with any one of the component displacements, and placing the tail of the second at the tip of the first. The outcome of this addition is called the 'resultant' of the two displacement vectors. The resultant is a vector that starts at the starting point and ends at the finishing point of this process.

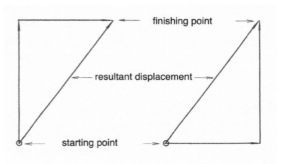

Exactly the same procedure can be used to determine the resultant *of any number* of like vectors acting in the same plane.

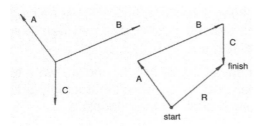

This diagram shows how to arrive at the resultant of three displacement vectors. Start with any one of them, and place the other vectors, tip to tail, in their correct directions. The vector (R on this diagram) that starts at the starting point and finishes at the tip of the last vector to be added, is the resultant.

All other types of vector, including forces, can be added in the same way.

Exercise

Solve this one using a graphical construction, to scale: A research ship leaves port and records its daily progress as follows: Day 1: it travels 200 km north-east; day two: 250 km east; day three: 180 km north-west; day four: 300 km south-west. Where is it in relation to port at the end of day four?

Vector addition of forces: resultants and equilibrants

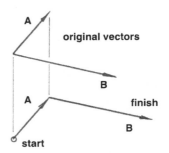

original vectors

Definition: The resultant of a set of forces

If a set of forces acting together can be replaced by one single force which has the same effect as all of them combined, then this force is called the resultant of that set.

To determine the resultant of two given co-planar forces, A and B, which act at the same point: start with any one of the forces, and draw its vector arrow in the appropriate direction. Now place the second one in such a position that its vector arrow starts where the first one ended.

The line joining the starting point to the finishing point represents the resultant of A and B. You will get the same resultant whether you start the diagram with force A or force B.

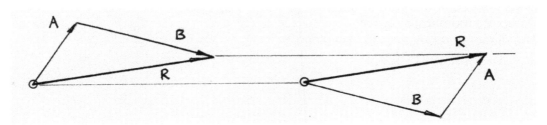

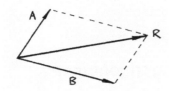

Hence, the resultant can be represented by the diagonal of a parallelogram with sides A and B. This is known as the parallelogram rule for the addition of vectors.

Determining the resultant of two forces by a graphical construction, using the parallelogram rule:

Example 1

Use a graphical method to determine the resultant of the following two forces:

Draw the vector diagram to scale. Complete the parallelogram. The diagonal represents the resultant, R.

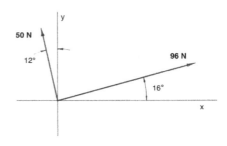

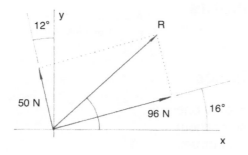

Measured to scale, from the diagram:

R = 111 N and Θ = 43°

Example 2

A flat raft is being pulled along the ground by men pulling on two ropes, in the directions shown. Determine:

The resultant of the two forces, and the direction in which the raft will move.

Draw the vector diagram to scale.
Complete the parallelogram.
The diagonal represents the resultant, R.

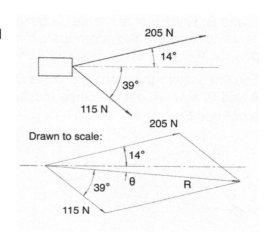

Drawn to scale:

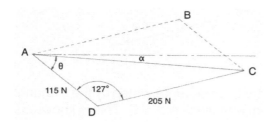

Measured to scale:

R = 289 N and α = 4.5 °

Determining the resultant of two forces, using trigonometry

For the example used above, instead of solving it by means of an accurate graphical construction, one could equally well do a rough sketch of the parallelogram and solve either of the two triangles that make up the parallelogram of forces, using trigonometry:

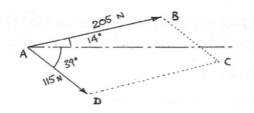

Complete a sketch of the parallelogram, and label the corners.

Since angle DAB = (39° + 14°) = 53°, it follows that angle ADC = 180° − 53° = 127°

Now, the triangle ADC is completely defined, since we have two sides and the included angle. Side AC of this triangle is the diagonal of the parallelogram, and represents the resultant, R, of the two forces.

Using the cosine rule in this triangle: $(AC)^2 = 115^2 + 205^2 - (2 \times 115 \times 205) \cos 127°$

∴ AC = 289.2 N (compare with 289 N previously obtained, graphically)

Using the sine rule in this triangle: $\sin θ/205 = \sin 127°/289.2$

∴ angle θ = 34.48°, and ∴ angle α = 4.52° (compare with 4.5° obtained graphically)

Exercise

Two forces act in the same plane as shown. Determine the magnitude and direction of their resultant using trigonometry, and confirm this result by a graphical construction.

[R = 1642 N, at an angle of 30.99° to the 1100 N force]

900 N

70°

1100 N

The resultant of more than two forces acting in the same plane

Suppose there are three forces: A, B and C, acting at a given point in the same plane. We could find the resultant of the three forces by first finding the resultant of A and B by the same method as above, and then adding that resultant to the third force C. This would look as follows:

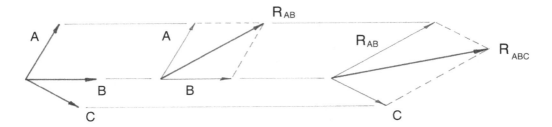

The same result would be obtained by drawing any one of these force vectors, to scale, and constructing a diagram showing the force vectors for the others, drawn to scale, tip-to-tail, following on the first one. The resultant, as we saw before, is that force which begins at the starting point and ends at the finishing point.

A diagram constructed in this way is called a *polygon of forces*. A polygon is a 'many-sided figure'. In drawing a polygon of forces, it makes no difference in which order the forces are drawn. As long as they are drawn, each in its correct direction, tip-to-tail, with their magnitudes properly represented to scale, the resultant will turn out the same.

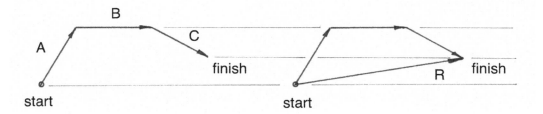

start

finish

start

R

finish

Below are three different arrangements of *the same three forces used in the preceding example*, showing that the resultant in each case is the same:

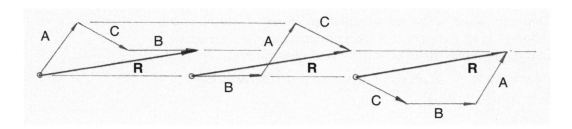

Exercises: resultants of more than two forces acting at a given point in the same plane

Question 1

Determine by a graphical construction the resultant of the following three co-planar forces acting at a point:

[175 N at 45° measured clockwise from the x-axis]

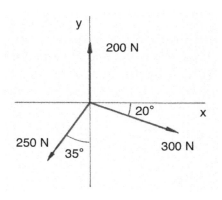

Question 2

A small steel ring is suspended in a rigid square frame by four guy-wires that can be tightened by turnbuckles. Three of the four wires are given the tensions shown on the diagram. The resultant of all the four tensions needs to be zero. Using a graphical method, determine the necessary tension in the fourth wire, and the angle θ.

[315 N and 24°, within acceptable graphical accuracy]

The equilibrant of a set of forces

If a set of forces acting at a point is in balance, namely, in equilibrium, its resultant must be zero. It follows that, if a set of forces is *not* in balance, it must have a non-zero resultant. Clearly, then, the additional force that would be needed to bring the set into balance, is a force that is equal and opposite to this resultant. This additional force, when added to the set, places the set in equilibrium, and is therefore called the *equilibrant* of the set of forces.

The diagram below shows a set of co-planar forces, A, B, C and D. Re-drawing them in the form of a polygon of forces, we can identify their resultant, R, as being that force which starts at the starting point of the open polygon, and ends at the finishing point of the open polygon. Since the equilibrant, E, of the set of forces is that force which is equal and opposite to the resultant, the equilibrant is that force which would *close* the polygon.

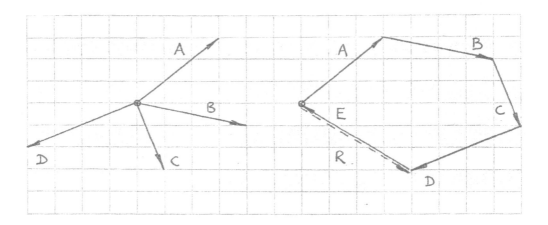

Vector Equations

A vector equation is a statement indicating which vectors, acting together, are collectively equivalent to a given vector, namely their resultant. For the forces in the preceding diagram, two vector equations may be written:

$$\vec{A} + \vec{B} + \vec{C} + \vec{D} = \vec{R} \quad \text{and} \quad \vec{A} + \vec{B} + \vec{C} + \vec{D} + \vec{E} = 0$$

A vector equation may have the appearance of an arithmetic sum, but it is definitely not an arithmetic statement of values, since the vectors appearing in it may have unique directions. It is common practice to indicate that a letter symbol represents a vector by drawing a short line or an arrow above the letter.

The components of a force

General components: We have seen that it is possible to find the resultant of any set of co-planar forces that act simultaneously. It is equally possible to work the other way: to start with a given force, F, and find a set of forces that, when acting together, have *the same effect* as the original force F. The forces that make up such a set are called the *components* of force F.

In the next illustration, forces A, B, C and D, acting together, are components of force F.

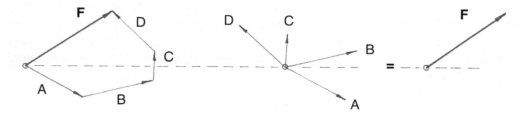

The components of a force can be arranged in a large variety of directions, relative to the original force. Below are illustrated three completely different arrangements of randomly selected components, each of which would combine to be equivalent to the given force F.

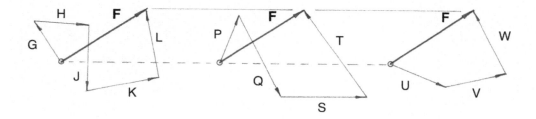

Force F in the above diagram was shown with respectively 5, 4 and 3 components. Suppose we examine the possible variations when there are only *two* components. In the next example, we show in each case *two* components that, acting together, have the same effect as the given force F. Each of the three forces F in the diagram is identical in magnitude and direction, but each has been given a *different* set of two components. Clearly the variations among sets of possible components are infinite.

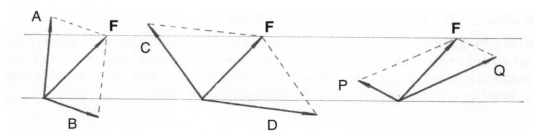

The two preceding diagrams illustrate the vector equations:

$$\vec{G} + \vec{H} + \vec{J} + \vec{K} + \vec{L} = \vec{F} \qquad \vec{P} + \vec{Q} + \vec{S} + \vec{T} = \vec{F} \qquad \vec{U} + \vec{V} + \vec{W} = \vec{F}$$

$$\text{and} \quad \vec{A} + \vec{B} = \vec{F} \qquad \vec{C} + \vec{D} = \vec{F} \quad \text{and} \quad \vec{P} + \vec{Q} = \vec{F}$$

Rectangular components of a force

For many purposes, when we need to determine the components of any given force, we are interested in identifying *two components that are at right angles to one another.*

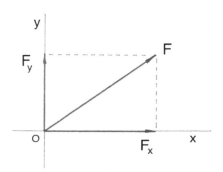

These are called *rectangular* components, and are useful because in any plane in which forces may occur, a force can be defined by the dimensions of its magnitude in two rectangular directions. Consider, for example, a force F acting in the x-y plane:

Any such force can have a component in the x-direction, F_x, and a component in the y-direction, F_y. These two rectangular components, acting together, have the same effect as the original force, and may therefore be considered to replace it.

Example

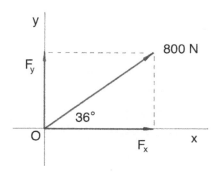

The 800 N force F shown here lies in the x-y plane. Determine the magnitudes of the rectangular components of this force that are respectively parallel to the x- axis and the y-axis.

$F_x/800 = \cos 36° \quad \therefore F_x = 800 \cos 36° = 647.2 \text{ N}$

$F_y/800 = \sin 36° \quad \therefore F_y = 800 \sin 36° = 470.2 \text{ N}$

When describing forces that are parallel to the axes of an x-y system of axes, it is important to specify that forces directed in the positive x-direction (or the positive y-direction) have positive values, while those in the negative directions have negative values.

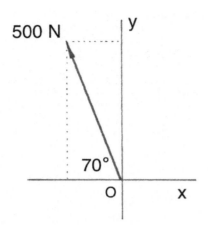

Example:

Resolve the 500 N force shown into rectangular components parallel to the x- and y- axes.

$$F_x = -(500 \cos 70°)$$
$$= -171.0 \text{ N}$$
$$F_y = 500 \sin 70°$$
$$= 469.8 \text{ N}$$

Example

A horizontal force of 100 N pushes against a brick resting on a plane inclined at 25° to the horizontal. Resolve the force into rectangular components that are respectively parallel and perpendicular to the plane.

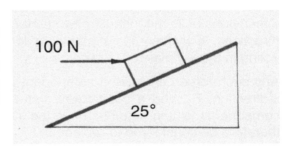

Draw a set of x-y axes in the required directions.

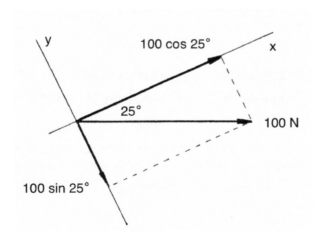

The rectangular components are:

In the x-direction.
100 cos (−25°) = 90.63 N

This component represents the amount of force pushing the brick upwards along the plane.

In the y-direction:

100 sin (−25°) = −42.26 N

This component represents the amount of force pushing the brick against the surface of the plane.

Exercises on determining rectangular components

Question 1

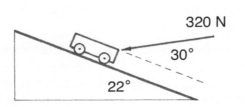

Determine the respective magnitudes of the components of the 320 N force that are available to push the trolley up the plane and against the surface of the plane. [277.1 N and 160.0 N]

Question 2

A brick is held against a vertical wall by force P. Write an expression for the magnitudes of each of the rectangular components of P that respectively push the brick against the wall and push the brick upwards along the wall surface. [P cos 40°; P sin 40°]

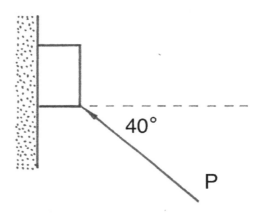

Question 3

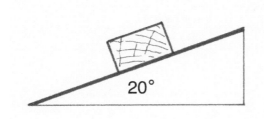

A 10 kg block of wood rests on an inclined plane. Determine the magnitudes of the rectangular components of the weight of the block that respectively push the block against the plane and push the block downwards along the surface of the plane.

[92.18 N; 33.55 N]

Determining the resultant of a set of co-planar forces by summation of rectangular components

The resultant of a number of co-planar forces can be determined by resolving all the forces into rectangular components in the x- and y- directions, and adding the values of the components in each of these respective directions.

The x-components and the y-components are added separately. The sum of the x-components is the x-component of the resultant. The sum of the y-components is the y-component of the resultant. To obtain the value and direction of the resultant, re-combine its two components. Care should be taken to label all components in the negative directions as negative.

Example

Determine the resultant of the following three forces in the x-y plane:

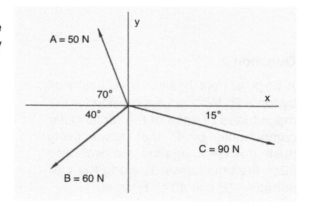

Make a table showing the magnitudes of the components of all the forces:

Force	x - component [N]	y - component [N]
A	− 50 cos 70°	50 sin 70°
B	− 60 cos 40°	− 60 sin 40°
C	90 cos 15°	− 90 sin 15°
Total	ΣFx = 23.87	ΣFy = −14.88

The totals in the table represent the respective magnitudes of the two components of the resultant. These two components can now be combined to obtain the resultant:

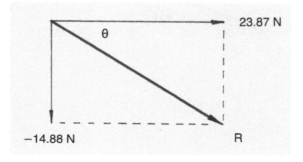

$\tan \theta = (14.88/23.87) \quad \therefore \theta = 31.94°$

$R^2 = \sqrt{(23.87^2 + 14.88^2)}$

$\therefore R = 28.13 \text{ N}$

Hence, the resultant of the three given forces is 28.13 N at an angle of 31.94° measured clockwise from the x-axis.

When asked to determine a force, it is necessary to specify the direction of that force. To simplify the way that directions are represented, there are certain conventions that can be used:

Three ways of describing the directions of vectors

The direction of any vector in a given plane needs to be specified relative to a reference line in that plane. Sometimes the reference line can be a given line on the original diagram that shows the physical arrangement of the objects under consideration. (As in 'the ladder makes an angle of 25° with the wall'.) However, since we are usually working on a set of orthogonal axes, it is customary to use one of the axes as a reference line.

Naturally, we can choose to make the x-axis coincide with a horizontal line, but we are free to direct it anywhere that is convenient in order to simplify the problem. Both of the arrangements shown here are valid.

Once our x-y axis system has been chosen, we can specify the direction of any line or vector relative to this axis set in any one of three ways:

1. Use the mathematical convention of considering the x-axis to be the reference line representing zero angle, and regard all angles measured anticlockwise from this line as positive.

2. Use the navigational method of specifying a 'bearing', which means using the line pointing due North as the reference, with all angles expressed as bearings, in degrees, proceeding clockwise from this line. It is usual to assume that the y-axis points North, unless otherwise specified.

3. Express a direction in terms of an acute angle between the vector and the most convenient of the four points of the compass. When employing this convention, it is assumed that North coincides with the y-axis.

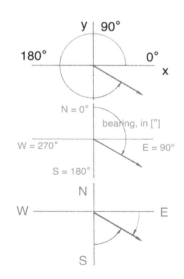

Hence, to describe the direction of the resultant in the preceding example, one could express the direction of the resultant as either – 31.94°, or on a bearing of 121.94°, or as E 31.94° S, which means: 'starting at East, move through 31.94° towards South'. It would also be correct to describe this angle as S 51.06° E.

Returning to the previous example, we can check the values of the magnitude and direction of the answer that was obtained through summing rectangular components, by drawing a force polygon to scale for the three given forces:

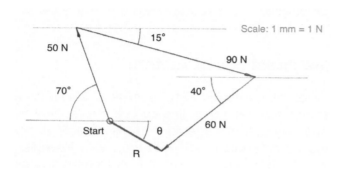

From the diagram, the resultant, measured to scale, is 29 N, at an angle E 32° S.

This is close enough to the calculated value to confirm it.

Exercises: determining the resultant of a set of forces by calculation, and checking the answer by means of a graphical construction

Question 1

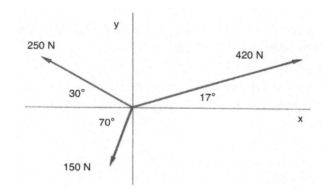

Determine the resultant of these three co-planar forces by summation of components.

Construct a polygon of forces to check the value you obtained in your calculations.

[R = 171.2 N;   E 38.59° N]

Question 2

Determine the resultant of the following three co-planar forces, by summation of components in the x- and y-directions. Check the validity of your answer by drawing the force polygon to scale.

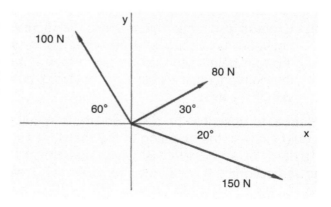

[R = 177.0 N, at angle E 25.17° N]

The principle of transmissibility of a force

To transmit means literally 'to send across', so if something is transmissible, that means it can be 'sent across'. The way this applies to forces is as follows:

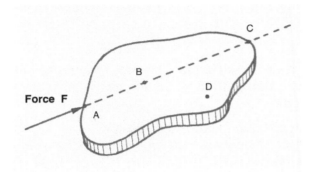

Any given force operates in a specific line of action. If this force acts on an object, it will have the same effect on the object, no matter *where* on this line of action the force is applied.

Consider the object shown here, with a force F acting on it. Force F has a line of action, indicated by the dotted line.

We could apply the force to point A, or to any other point along the same line of action, say B or C. As long as the point of application is on this line, the force will have exactly the same effect on the object.

If we were to apply the force F to any other point, D, that is *not* on this line of action, the force would have a completely different effect on the object, due to the different rotational effect that would be produced.

Since applying the force to point A has the same effect as applying it to point C, it follows that if the object were a particle (point mass), then a force pushing it from the left would be equivalent to a force pulling it from the right.

 is completely equivalent to

When determining the resultant of any set of co-planar forces acting at a point, it is sometimes easier to keep track of the components if all the forces are directed *away* from the common point. It is therefore quite acceptable to move any force along its line of action so that it can be indicated as pulling rather than pushing on the common point. For example, in the diagram below, the set of forces indicated on the right is equivalent to the set shown on the left:

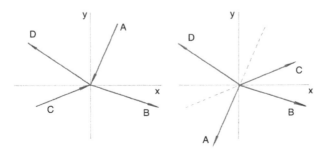

Equilibrium conditions for a particle in 2-D

Any particle will be in equilibrium if the resultant of all the forces acting on it is zero. It follows that if a particle is *known* to be in equilibrium, the resultant of all the forces acting on it *must* be zero. This principle is of great use in analysing co-planar forces that act at a point.

Example

Three ropes are tied to a small light ring, as shown below. The upper two ropes are fixed to walls, and the lower one carries a load of 1000 N. Determine the respective tensions, A and B, in the upper two ropes.

In this situation, the ring is clearly in equilibrium. Hence the resultant of all forces acting on the ring must be zero. Therefore, if we draw a polygon of forces for all the forces acting on the ring, this polygon *must close*.

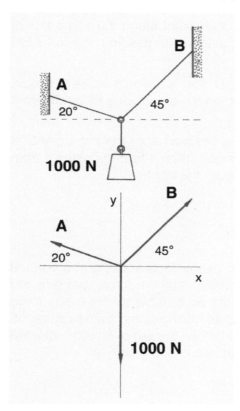

First, draw a force diagram, showing the three forces radiating from the ring. Work from this diagram to arrange the polygon of forces.

Since there are only three forces acting, this polygon simplifies to a triangle.

A force polygon that comprises only three forces is known as the *triangle of forces*.

Draw the triangle, showing each force in its correct direction, tip-to-tail. Determine the values of the unknown forces, either by using trigonometry, or by drawing the diagram accurately, to scale, and measuring the forces, to scale.

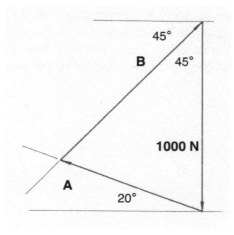

[A = 780.2 N and B = 1037 N]

Exercises on the triangle of forces

In each of the following exercises, identify one particle that is in equilibrium under the action of three forces. Then draw a force diagram of the forces acting at this point. Rearrange these forces to form a triangle of forces, and determine the values of the unknown forces or angles by solving this triangle, using trigonometry. Check your answers by drawing the triangles to scale.

Question 1

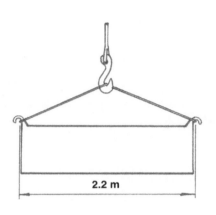

2.2 m

A skip with a mass of 2 tonnes is suspended from a crane hook by means of a sling whose end loops are placed over lugs on the skip.

Determine the tension in the sling, if the length of the sling is firstly: 2.4 m, and secondly: 3.6 m.   [24.55 kN   and 12.39 kN respectively]

Is it safer to use a longer sling, or a shorter sling, if given the choice?

Question 2

A load of 10 kN is suspended from a crane. The crane rope is pulled to one side by a horizontal force F, causing the upper part of the crane rope to make an angle of 10° with the vertical. Determine:

The magnitude of force F, and

The tension in the upper part of the crane rope.

[1.763 kN and 10.15 kN]

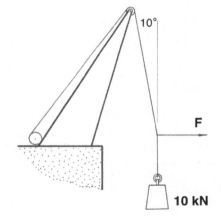

10°

F

10 kN

Question 3

A small block weighing 100 N is placed on a frictionless slope that makes an angle of 30° with the horizontal. Determine the magnitude of a horizontal force F that will keep the block in equilibrium.   [57.74 N]

F

30°

Equilibrium equations for a particle in 2-D

We have seen that if a particle is in equilibrium under the action of a set of forces, the resultant of that set must be zero. This means that *both* the x-component of the resultant *and* the y-component of the resultant must be zero.

If the x-component of the resultant of a set of forces is zero, the sum of all the x-components of the forces in that set must be zero. The same applies in the y-direction. These statements result in the equations:

$\Sigma F_x = 0$ and $\Sigma F_y = 0$

which both apply to any particle that is in equilibrium.

Example

The small ring shown below is tied to four ropes, three of which are attached to weights. The fourth rope, D, is attached to a fixed point.

The system comes to rest in the position shown. Determine the value of the tension in rope D and the angle θ that it makes with the horizontal, in the rest position.

Consider the masses of the sheaves and the ropes, and the friction in the sheaves, to be negligible.

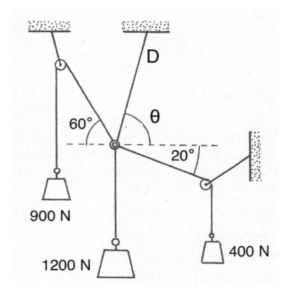

Solution

The ring is in equilibrium under the action of four forces. Draw a diagram showing the four forces acting on the ring, and apply the equations

$\Sigma F_x = 0$ and $\Sigma F_y = 0$.

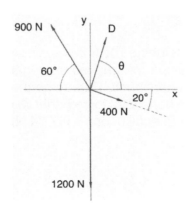

$\Sigma F_x = 0$, ∴ 400 cos 20° + D cos θ − 900 cos 60° = 0

∴ D cos θ = 74.123 ....(1)

$\Sigma F_y = 0$, ∴ 900 sin 60° + D sin θ − 1200 − 400 sin 20° = 0

∴ D sin θ = 557.385 ....(2)

(2) ÷ (1):   tan θ = 557.385/ 74.123   ∴ θ = 82.43°

From (1):   D = 74.123/cos 82.43° = 562.3 N

Limitations of the use of a polygon of forces

Since the equilibrium of a particle subjected to coplanar forces is governed by only two equations, namely $\Sigma F_x = 0$ and $\Sigma F_y = 0$, the maximum number of unknowns that can be solved for, either by the use of these equations, or by drawing a polygon of forces to scale, is *two*.

This means that, in any exercise of this type, it will be possible to solve for either two force magnitudes, or two angles, or one force magnitude and one angle. If there are three or more unknown variables, no solution will be possible.

Exercises on three forces acting at a point, in equilibrium

Question 1

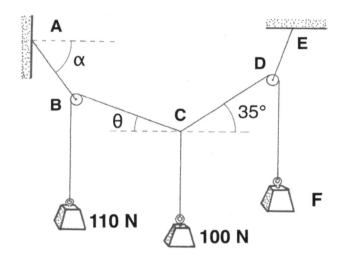

Three load-bearing ropes are tied together at point C.

Two of the ropes pass over light, frictionless sheaves attached to a frame by ropes AB and DE.

The system comes to rest in the position shown.

Determine:

a. The tension in rope BC [110 N]

b. The value of the mass-piece at F   [13.51 kg]

c. The value of angle θ   [11.5°]

d. The tension in rope AB   [172 N]

e. The value of angle α   [51°]

85

Question 2

The three coplanar forces shown here are in equilibrium. Use a graphical construction to determine the values of force F and angle β that will satisfy the conditions of equilibrium.

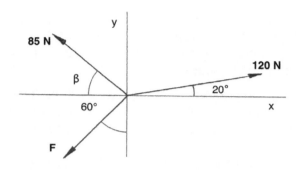

[There are two solutions: either

$F = 51.5$ N and $β = 11°$, or

$F = 136.5$ N and $β = 71.5°$]

These values were obtained graphically. Your answers might differ slightly.

Conclusion

In this chapter we have examined the nature of forces, and have exercised techniques for determining unknown forces among a set of forces acting on a particle that is in equilibrium.

Thus far our workings have been confined to 2-dimensional examples. It is virtually impossible to apply *graphical* solutions to solve for forces in 3-D situations, as such problems require simultaneous solutions for force polygons in three orthogonal planes. This is not practicable when working in the single plane of a sheet of paper.

In cases where the data is suitable, 3-D problems dealing with the equilibrium of a single particle can be solved using the equations: $\Sigma F_x = 0$; $\Sigma F_y = 0$ and $\Sigma F_z = 0$. In such cases, since we have three equations, we are able to solve for a *maximum* of three unknowns.

In a later chapter on 'Forces in Structures', a technique will be demonstrated for solving for unknown forces acting at a point in 3-D. For the present, however, we will continue to deal with forces acting in a single plane.

The following chapter deals with force moments, torque, static equilibrium of solid bodies, and the free-body diagram, which is an indispensable tool for anyone needing to analyse forces.

Chapter 5

Force moments, torque, equilibrium of rigid bodies and free-body diagrams

- *Definition of a force moment and a torque*
- *Equilibrium conditions for a solid object*
- *Free-body diagrams*
- *Constraints on the equilibrium of solid objects*
- *Equilibrium of beams under load*

The moment of a force

The expression 'moment of a force' is used in mechanics to mean 'the rotating effect produced by a force'. The moment of a force about a given point is the product of the magnitude of the force and the shortest distance between the given point and the line of action of the force.

When stating the value of a force moment, it is essential to specify about which point a moment is being measured, and whether the moment is clockwise or anticlockwise.

In this diagram, the moment of the 600 N force about point A is (600 N x 2 m), namely 1200 Nm clockwise. This is denoted as M_A = 1200 Nm ⤵.

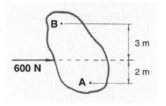

The moment of this same force about point B is (600 N x 3 m), namely 1800 Nm anticlockwise, denoted as M_B = 1800 Nm ⤴.

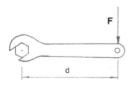

It is easy to relate to force moments when we think of tightening a nut with a spanner. We know from experience that the greater the force F we exert, and the greater is dimension d, the greater will be the turning effect we can exert on the nut. The moment of the force we can apply is F x d.

In each of the diagrams at right, the moment of the force F about point O is given by:

M_o = F x d, clockwise.

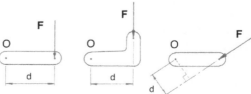

The moment of an oblique force

Sometimes a force is directed at an angle to the line joining its point of application to the point about which moments are being determined. In such cases, the moment about that point may determined by either of two methods, as follows:

First method: consider the physical dimensions of the triangle formed by the line of action of the force and dimension 'd'.

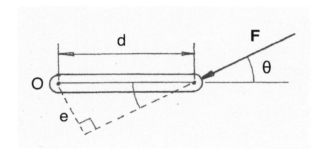

In the right angled triangle so formed,

$e/d = \sin \theta$ $\therefore e = d \sin \theta$
and

$M_0 = F.e = F(d \sin\theta) = Fd \sin\theta$ ↘

Second method: resolve the force F into components parallel to and perpendicular to the line whose dimension is 'd':

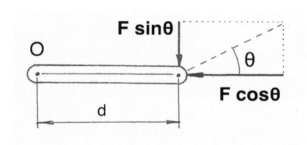

Of these two components, (F cos θ) has zero moment about point O, because its line of action passes through point O.

However, the other component, F sinθ, has a moment about point O:

$M_0 = (F \sin \theta)d = Fd \sin\theta$ ↘

Two approaches, same result.

Exercises on determining force moments

The next two diagrams show various plates and levers, each with a number of forces acting on them. In each case, confirm that the sum of the moments about point O (namely, ΣM_0) has the value stated below the diagram.

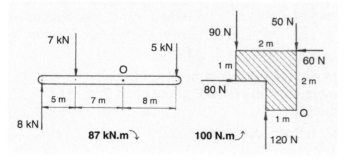

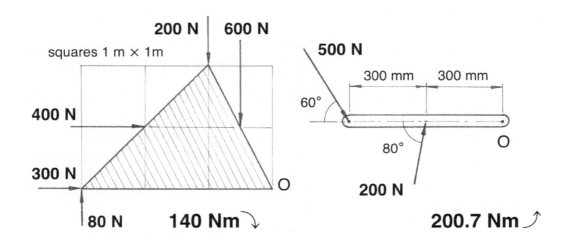

200 N | **600 N**

squares 1 m × 1m

400 N

300 N

80 N   **140 Nm** ↘

500 N

300 mm   300 mm

60°

80°

O

200 N

200.7 Nm ↗

The moment of a 'force couple'

Two co-planar forces, equal and opposite, whose lines of action are parallel, but which do not coincide, form what is known as a 'force couple'.

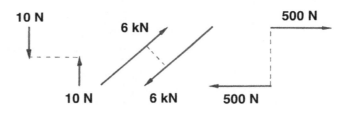

10 N

6 kN

500 N

10 N   6 kN   500 N

The effect of a couple on an object is *purely* rotational. Since the two forces are equal and opposite, their translational effects cancel one another. The purely twisting effect of a couple can be illustrated by the rotation of a drum-major's mace, as a result of the opposing forces exerted by finger and thumb. (Naturally, the weight of the mace still has to be supported as well.)

The turning effect, or moment, produced by a couple is the product of any *one* of the forces and the distance between them. In the diagram below, the sum of the moments about the centre-point is:

F

P — d/2 ¦ d/2 — Q

O

F

Anticlockwise: (F x d/2) + (F x d/2)
Therefore: $\Sigma M_o = 2(F \times d/2) = F \, d$ ↗

The moment of the couple about either of the points P or Q is also Fd ↗.

Definition of a torque

One often hears about torque, as a rotational effect. A torque wrench is a tool that imparts a measurable amount of torque to a nut that is being tightened. Engines are rated in terms of how much torque they can deliver. The units of torque are the same as the units of a force moment, namely Nm. So, what is a 'torque', and how does it differ from a force moment?

The effects of a torque and a force moment are precisely the same: they are both efforts to impart rotational motion. They differ only in this sense: a force moment arises when a known force acts at a known distance from a rotation axis. A torque, on the other hand, arises when forces of an unspecified magnitude act at an unspecified radius from the rotation axis.

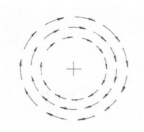

For example, consider the way in which an electric motor is made to turn. A current passes through windings in an armature, generating an electro-motive force in each winding. The windings are arranged so that these forces are all in the same rotational direction. The windings are not usually all at the same radius from the rotation axis. But the cumulative force moments from all the windings add up to a total turning effect which we call a torque.

Likewise, if you use a screwdriver to drive a wood-screw into a piece of wood, simply by the way you rotate your wrist, you impart a turning effect, called a torque. In this situation, it is not possible to isolate a single force that acts at a single exact radius, to describe the force moment applied to the screw. However, the turning effect is the same, and the units in which they are measured are the same. So, torques are equivalent to force moments.

Equilibrium conditions for a rigid, solid object

Naturally, if an object has a net moment acting on it, it will experience rotational acceleration, and is therefore not in equilibrium. So, a condition for the equilibrium of any solid object that has dimensions (as opposed to a particle), is that the sum of the moments *about any point O on the object* must be zero.

The equation that expresses this condition is: $\Sigma M_o = 0$

It is important to realise that point O can be chosen *anywhere* on the object. If an object is in equilibrium, you cannot have the sum of the moments about one point being zero, while the sum of the moments about another point is not zero. If you do have such a circumstance, then the object is *not* in equilibrium.

For a solid object to be in equilibrium *in a single plane* (the x-y plane), all three of the following conditions must apply, namely: $\Sigma F_x = 0$ and $\Sigma F_y = 0$ and $\Sigma M_o = 0$

Naturally, if we are considering the possible equilibrium of an object in 3 dimensions, we would need to include similar equations that apply to the x-z and y-z planes. However, the treatment that follows will remain confined to dealing with equilibrium in a single plane.

Example:

A rectangular plate, 800 mm x 600 mm, weighing 150 N, is held in equilibrium in a vertical plane by the forces shown on the diagram.

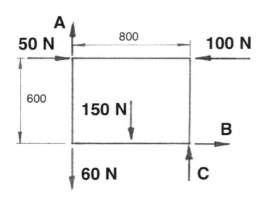

Determine the magnitudes and directions of the three unknown forces, A, B and C.

Check your answers by evaluating the moments about any point other than the one you initially chose as point 'O'.

Solution:

The three conditions for equilibrium must all apply simultaneously, namely

$\Sigma F_x = 0$ and $\Sigma F_y = 0$ and $\Sigma M_o = 0$

Set up each of these three equations according to the given data:

In the x-direction: $\Sigma F_x = 0$ therefore $50 - 100 + B = 0$ ....(1)

Which yields: B = −50 N. The negative sign here means simply that force B is in the opposite direction to that assumed on the diagram. So, force B must be 50 N *to the left.*

In the y-direction: $\Sigma F_y = 0$ therefore $A + C - 150 - 60 = 0$ ....(2)

When applying the equation $\Sigma M_o = 0$, we can choose any point 'O' about which to take moments. The easiest point to choose is one through which most of the unknown forces pass. Reason: if a force passes through a point, its moment about that point is zero. The obvious point to choose is the lower right hand corner of the plate, since both the given unknown forces B and C pass through this corner. Label this point as 'O', and choose clockwise as the positive direction for moments: The equation $\Sigma M_o = 0$ becomes:

$(A \times 800) + (50 \times 600) - (60 \times 800) - (150 \times 400) - (100 \times 600) = 0$ ....(3)

Which yields: A = 172.5 N

Substituting this value into (2) yields the value C = 37.5 N

Now check whether the sum of the moments about any other point is zero. Consider, for example, point P at the top left corner of the plate.

$\Sigma M_p = (150 \times 400) - (37.5 \times 800) - (50 \times 600) = 0$

Try another point, say point Q at the lower left corner of the plate:

$\Sigma M_Q = (50 \times 600) + (150 \times 400) - (100 \times 600) - (37.5 \times 800) = 0$

No matter which point we select, we find that the sum of the moments about that point on the plate is zero. This finding reinforces for us the fact that if an object is in equilibrium, the sum of the moments *about any point on it* must be zero. Hence, when we set up the equation $\Sigma M_o = 0$, we always have the choice of which point to use as the point about which to consider moments.

Exercise: The triangular plate shown here has negligible mass. It is in equilibrium under the action of the forces shown. Determine the values of the three unknown forces, A, B and C.

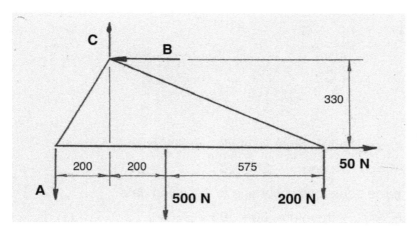

[A = 1362.5 N;

B = 50 N; and

C = 2062.5 N]

Free-Body Diagrams (FBDs)

The diagram of the plate in the example above is what we call a free-body diagram. It is called thus because it shows only one object, freed from its surroundings, together with all the forces acting on the object.

A free-body diagram is an essential tool for analysing the forces acting on an object. You will need to be able to draw a free-body diagram at every level of your engineering course, and every time you do a force analysis for a new situation in your engineering career.

To solve for any unknown forces that act on an object, it is essential to start by drawing a FBD of the object, using the given data. In the above example, the data was presented already in the form of a FBD, but this is not usually the case. Normally, when you are required to analyse the forces acting on an object, a free-body diagram is not provided, and has to be drawn before you can set up the equations of equilibrium for the object.

Without a FBD to guide you in setting up the equilibrium equations, it is easy to get confused about which forces need to be considered. In particular, students are likely to become confused between the forces acting on an object, and the forces which that object exerts on its surroundings. If you always draw a FBD, before trying to set up the equations of equilibrium, you will not get confused.

There are three rules for drawing a free-body diagram:

Draw one object only, freed from its surroundings;

Show all the forces acting *on* that object; and

Do NOT show any forces which that object exerts on its surroundings.

Remember that the weight of an object is a force acting *on* it, and should always be included in a FBD.

Example:

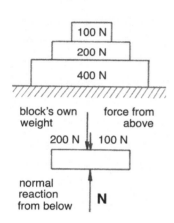

Three blocks of indicated weight are placed in a stack on a table. Draw a FBD of the middle block, and determine the value of the normal reaction on that block from the block below it.

Solution: Draw the middle block on its own. Show only the forces that act *on* it. These forces include the block's own weight, and the normal reaction from the blocks above and below it.

The FBD of the middle block looks as shown here:

From which, we can deduce that the normal reaction, **N** exerted on the middle block from below, must be 300 N.

Example:

The lever shown here is in equilibrium. Draw a free-body diagram of the lever and use the FBD to determine the value of force J and the magnitude and direction of the force that the hinge-pin exerts on the lever.

Solution:

We need to include *all* the forces that act on the lever. The hinge-pin will exert a force F on the lever. Since we do not know the direction of force F, we let it consist of two rectangular components, F_x and F_y.

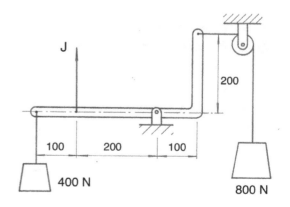

The complete FBD looks as follows:

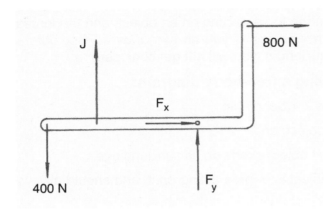

To solve for the value of force J, apply the equation $\Sigma M_o = 0$. It makes sense to choose the moment pivot point 'O' to be at the centre of the hinge-pin, so that the moments of F_x and F_y about that point are both zero.

Then, since $\Sigma M_o = 0$:

$(800 \times 200) + (J \times 200) - (400 \times 300) = 0$

Which yields J = −200 N, namely 200 N in the opposite direction to which it was shown in the diagram, so J = 200 N downwards.

We have solved for one unknown, and our equations will allow us to solve for two more. To determine the values of F_x and F_y, we apply the other two equations of equilibrium, namely $\Sigma F_x = 0$ and $\Sigma F_y = 0$. You can check that the answers are as follows:

F_x = 800 N to the left, and

F_y = 600 N upwards

We now re-combine these two components to obtain a single force F, which works out to be 1000 N at an angle of N 53.13° W. Note that, like all the other forces on the FBD, this is a force acting *on* the lever.

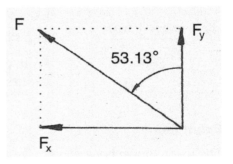

(Naturally, the lever will exert an equal and opposite force on the hinge-pin.)

Example:

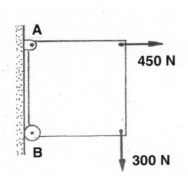

A square steel plate, weighing 400 N, has a small hole drilled through it, near each corner. The holes form the corners of a square 500 mm x 500 mm. At holes A and B are placed respectively a hinge and a roller, which support the plate in a vertical plane. Two additional loads are applied at the other two holes.

Determine the magnitude and direction of the force that the hinge pin exerts on the plate, and the force that the roller exerts on the wall.

94

Solution:

Draw a FBD of the plate. This shows *only* the plate and the forces acting on it. You should *not* show the hinge, the hinge pin, the roller, the roller pin, or the wall. Rule 1 for drawing a FBD: *one object only.*

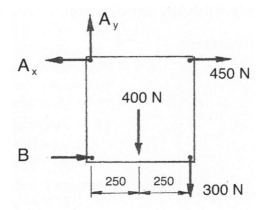

If a force is unknown, draw it in, and name it. The hinge pin at A would be exerting a force of unknown direction on the plate. Call the rectangular components of this force A_x and A_y. Show both of these components.

When recombined, these two components will give us the single force A that the hinge pin exerts on the plate.

The force exerted by the roller pin at B must be purely horizontal. This is due to the fact that the roller, pushing as it does against a vertical wall, cannot sustain a force that has a vertical component. If there is a vertical force on the roller, the roller will simply roll out of the way.

Apply the three equations for equilibrium:

$\Sigma F_x = 0$ $\therefore$ $450 + B - A_x = 0$ ....(1)

$\Sigma F_y = 0$ $\therefore$ $A_y - 400 - 300 = 0$ ....(2)

$\Sigma M_o = 0$ $\therefore$ $(300 \times 500) + (400 \times 250) - (B \times 500) = 0$..................(3)

Solving these three equations simultaneously, yields the values

$A_x = 950$ N; $A_y = 700$ N; $B = 500$ N

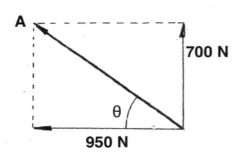

Recombining the components of force A:

$A = \sqrt{[950^2 + 700^2]} = 1180$ N

Angle $\theta = \tan^{-1}(700/950) = 36.38°$

Further, the force that the roller exerts on the wall is equal and opposite to the force that the wall exerts on the roller, namely 500 N to the left.

Exercises on the use of FBDs to solve for unknowns in equilibrium conditions:

Question 1

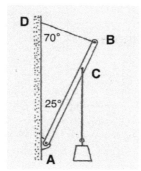

The strut of a wall-crane consists of a pole weighing120 N, hinged at point A and supported by a rope at point B. A load of 600 N is suspended from point C. AC = 3 m; CB = 1 m.

Draw a FBD of the pole and use it to determine the tension in the rope BD and the magnitude and direction of the force that the hinge-pin exerts on the pole.

[Tension in rope BD = 152.7 N; force exerted by hinge-pin = 683.0 N at angle E 77.87° N]

Question 2

A solid plate, ABC, of negligible weight, acts as a crane boom. This plate is hinged to a fixed base at point C. AD is a wire rope anchoring the boom to the base, and is in line with AB. The crane carries a 10 kN load. AC = 2 m; BC = 4 m.

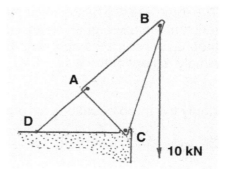

Draw a FBD of the plate, and use it to determine the tension in the rope AD, as well as the magnitude and direction of the force that the hinge pin exerts on the crane boom at C.
[5.18 kN; 14.15 kN; E 75° N]

Constraints on the equilibrium of solid objects

We have seen that there are 3 equations for the equilibrium of a solid object in a given plane, namely: $\Sigma F_x = 0$ and $\Sigma F_y = 0$ and $\Sigma M_o = 0$. These enable us to solve for up to three unknown forces. However, if there are *more* than 3 unknown forces, we cannot solve for the unknowns. If an object is acted on by *more* than three unknown

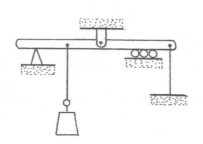

forces, we say the object is 'over-constrained', or 'statically indeterminate' (meaning it cannot be solved using the equations of statics, namely the above three equations).

For example, the beam illustrated here is supported by a knife-edge, a roller, a hinge and a wire. It will be impossible to determine the forces in all of the supports, using only the three equations at our disposal. This beam might be in equilibrium, but has *more* forces acting on it than are *needed* for equilibrium, and is therefore over-constrained.

It is important to know what kind of constraints are placed upon a solid object by different kinds of supports. If a given support is capable of exerting only a force in the x-direction, it offers one constraint. If it can also exert a force in the y-direction, it offers two constraints. If a support is also capable of exerting a moment on the solid object, it offers a third constraint.

If you know what kind of constraints a particular support provides, you can fill in on the FBD the vector arrows representing the appropriate unknown forces or moments. This table lists examples of the constraints offered by various common supports:

Type of support	symbol	Forces this type of support can sustain	Number of constraints provided
Rollers		A force at right angles to the supported surface	1
A rope, wire or link of known direction		A force in the same direction as the rope/wire/link	1
A collar on a smooth rod		A force at right angles to the rod	1
Knife edge		A force of unknown direction.	2
Rough surface		A force of unknown direction	2
Hinge		A force of unknown direction	2
Fixed support, as in a beam end built into a wall.		Exerts forces that are distributed over the area of contact. Collectively, these are equivalent to a force of unknown direction, plus a couple.	3

Equilibrium of beams

A beam under load is a particular example of a solid object in equilibrium. If we know the loading on a beam, we can determine the reactions needed at the points of support to keep the beam in equilibrium. The first step in solving a beam problem is to draw a free-body diagram of the beam. This FBD should always be drawn separately, *not* superimposed on the given loading diagram.

Example:

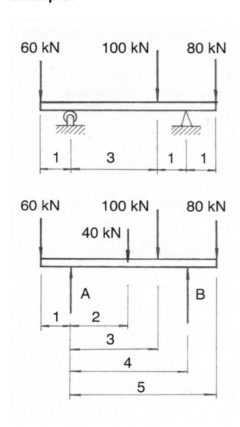

The beam shown here weighs 40 kN, and is supported on a roller at point A and a knife-edged support at point B. Given that there are three known point loads on the beam, as shown, determine the reactions at points A and B.

The reactions at the supports are the forces that the support points exert *on* the beam. Since they are forces acting *on* the beam, they must be included in a FBD of the beam.

Another force that acts *on* the beam is its weight, which must therefore also appear on the FBD of the beam. The weight acts as a point load, passing through the centre of gravity of the beam.

Draw the FBD, to scale, directly below the given diagram.

A knife-edged support is usually capable of exerting a sideways force on a beam, but, in view of the fact that there are no other forces acting on this beam that have a component in the x-direction, in this case we can safely conclude that the reaction at this knife edge is entirely vertical.

From the FBD, we set up the equations for equilibrium. In this case, there are no forces acting in the x-direction, so we have only two equations, namely:

$\Sigma F_y = 0$:   Thus $A + B - 280 = 0$ .... (1), and

$\Sigma M_A = 0$:   Choosing clockwise moments as positive, we get:

$(40 \times 2) + (100 \times 3) + (80 \times 5) - (B \times 4) - (60 \times 1) = 0$ .... (2)

Solving equation (2), yields B = 180 kN

Substituting this value into (1) yields: A = 100 kN

Exercise:

For this 50 kN beam with the given loading, determine the reactions at the knife-edged supports P and Q. The dimensions given are in metres.

[P = 220 kN and Q = 350 kN]

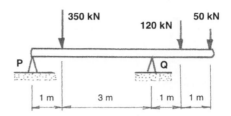

Example:

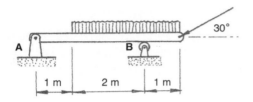

A beam weighing 40 kN is hinged at point A and is supported by a roller at point B. The beam carries a distributed load of 20 kN/m over part of its length, as shown, as well one oblique load of 50 kN. Determine the forces that the hinge-pin and the roller exert on the beam. All dimensions are in metres.

Solution:

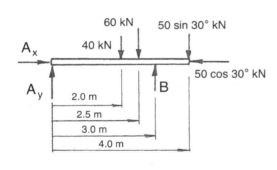

All distributed loads, including the weight of the beam, can be assumed to act as point loads, placed at the centre of mass of the respective load.

The unknown forces on the FBD are represented as shown here:

The hinge pin exerts a force, 'A' of unknown direction on the beam, and therefore this force has both an x- and a y-component. Draw and label them on the FBD as A_x and A_y.

The roller can sustain only an upward force, so the force 'B' that the roller exerts on the beam has to be in the y-direction.

$\Sigma M_A = 0$, hence $(40 \times 2) + (60 \times 2.5) + (50 \sin 30° \times 4) - (B \times 3) = 0$ ∴ B = 110 kN

$\Sigma F_y = 0$, hence $A_y + 110 - 40 - 60 - 50 \sin 30° = 0$ therefore $A_y = 15$ kN

$\Sigma F_x = 0$, hence $A_x - 50 \cos 30° = 0$

therefore $A_x = 43.30$ kN

Re-combining the two components of force A:

A = 45.83 kN,   E 19.10° N

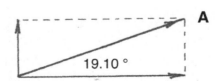

Example: cantilever beam (namely, a beam with one end built into a wall)

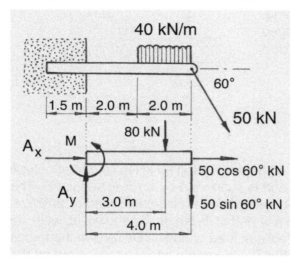

Determine the reactions at the support for this beam. The beam carries a distributed load and one oblique point load, as shown. Ignore the weight of the beam.

Solution: Draw the free-body diagram of the beam, showing *only* the part of the beam protruding from the wall.

Let the wall exert forces A_x, A_y and a moment M on the beam.

By inspection, moment M would appear to be anticlockwise, so it is reasonable to indicate it as such.

If we assume an incorrect sense for this moment, our calculations will simply produce a negative value for the moment, indicating that the moment acting on the beam must be opposite to the assumed direction.

$\Sigma M_A = 0$, hence $\quad M - (80 \times 3) - (50 \sin 60° \times 4) = 0$

$$\therefore M = (80 \times 3) + (50 \sin 60° \times 4) = 413.2 \text{ kNm.}$$

$\Sigma F_y = 0$, hence $\quad A_y - 80 - 50 \sin 60° = 0 \quad \therefore A_y = 123.3 \text{ kN}$

$\Sigma F_x = 0$, hence $\quad A_x + 50 \cos 60° = 0 \quad \therefore A_x = -25 \text{ kN}$, namely 25 kN to the left.

The force moment 'M' will actually be provided by a distributed force exerted by the wall, continuous over the built-in section of the beam, as indicated on the left below:

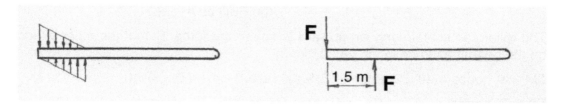

As an approximation to this arrangement, suppose the moment were provided by an equivalent couple, consisting of two parallel forces 'F', as shown on the right. Since the moment of this couple must be equal to the moment 'M', we have F × 1.5 m = 413.2 kNm, which gives the value 275.5 kN for each of the two forces 'F'.

If we include these forces on a FBD of the whole beam, (this time incorporating the part built into the wall), we will find that the beam is in equilibrium.

The complete FBD of the beam, replacing the moment at the wall with two forces forming a couple, would look as follows:

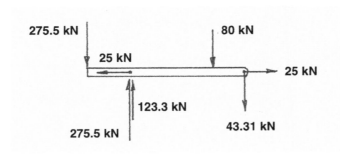

The distance between the two forces 'F' is equal to the depth to which the beam penetrates the wall.

The shorter this distance, the greater will be the value of 'F', and the more likely it is that the beam will crush the wall at its point of insertion.

At that point the localised downward force that the beam exerts on the wall will be 275.5 kN + 123.3 kN, namely 398.8 kN.

Exercises: solving equilibrium situations using free-body diagrams

Question 1

The beam shown here weighs 9 kN/m. It carries a point load of 120 kN and a distributed load of 24 kN/m. Draw a FBD of the beam, and use it to determine the reactions at supports A and B.

[A = 38 kN; B = 226 kN]

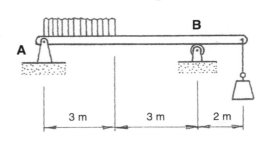

Question 2

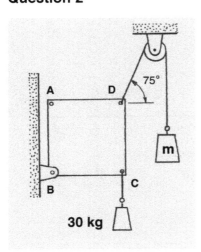

This square steel plate, 800 mm × 800 mm between the corner holes, and with mass 60 kg, is hinged at B, and has loads applied at points C and D. It is in equilibrium in the position shown. The sheave may be considered frictionless.

Draw the FBD of the plate, and determine:

The value of mass m necessary for equilibrium, and The force exerted on the plate by the hinge-pin at B.

[84.85 kg; 553.3 N at angle W 67.09° S]

Question 3

The boom, BC, of a wall-crane weighs 8 kN. It is supported by a wire rope AC, and carries a single concentrated load, as shown.

Draw the FBD of this boom, and determine:

The tension, F, in the rope, and
The reaction that the hinge-pin exerts on the boom

[F = 49.88 kN; 32.21 kN at angle E 30.81° N]

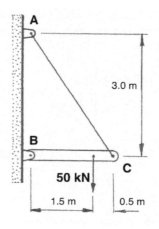

Question 4

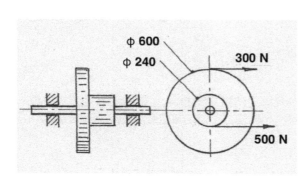

A compound wheel with an integral shaft has ropes wound around its two larger circumferences, being pulled in the directions shown. Determine:

The value of the torque that must be applied to the shaft to prevent this wheel from rotating. [60 Nm↗]

The value of the horizontal force that the shaft exerts on its bearings under this loading.   [800 N]

Question 5

A cantilever beam weighs 250 kN and is loaded as shown.

Determine:

- The reaction that the wall exerts on the beam. [an upward force of 750 N plus a clockwise moment of 2500 Nm]

- The maximum crushing force on the wall material at any point where the beam is in contact with the wall. [3250 kN]

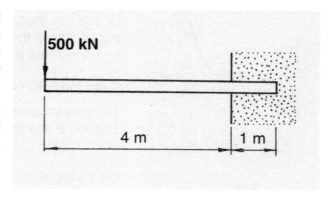

102

Question 6

A pair of tongs is being used to grip a piece of metal bar. Draw FBDs of each of the following parts: the right arm of the tongs, the piece of bar, the left arm of the tongs, and the hinge pin. Label all forces in multiples of force **F**. Ignore the weight of the constituent parts of this arrangement.

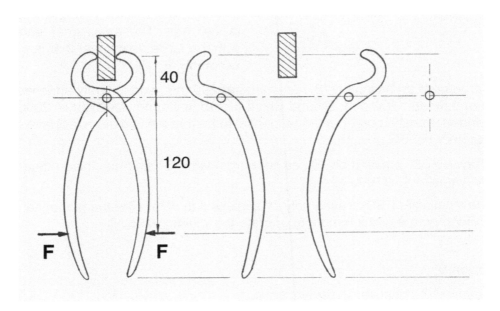

Question 7

The rectangular flat plate shown weighs 1000 N. It has five small holes drilled through it: one at each corner and one at point P. The holes are small enough not to affect the location of the centre of gravity of the plate.

The plate is hinged to a wall at point D and supported by a wire rope AB, while carrying an extra load of 500 N suspended from point P.

Draw a FBD of the plate, showing all forces resolved into vertical and horizontal components. Determine the tension in rope AB. [931.3 N]

Determine the vertical and horizontal components, respectively, of the force that the hinge pin exerts on the plate. [1106 N upwards; 844 N to the right]

Question 8

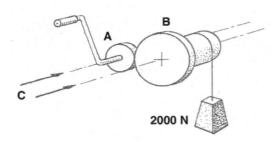

Shown here is a schematic diagram of a geared hoist.

Assembly 'A' consists of a crank handle attached to a small gearwheel, of diameter 60 mm. The crank radius is 240 mm. The small gear engages with the large gearwheel that is part of assembly 'B'.

The large gear on assembly 'B' has diameter 200 mm, and is firmly attached to a drum of diameter 100 mm, around which a cord is wound. A weight of 2000 N is suspended from the cord. Let the tangential force that the two gearwheels exert on one another be 'F'.

a. Draw a FBD of assembly 'B', as seen from view 'C', and use this to determine the value of F. [1000 N]

b. Draw a similar FBD of assembly 'A' and use it to determine the tangential force needed on the crank handle to operate the winch. [125 N]

Question 9

The beam AB consists of square section solid steel, 100 mm × 100 mm. Determine:

The tension in the wire rope BC. [1767 N]

The horizontal pull on the hinge pin at A. [883.6 N]

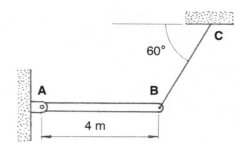

Question 10

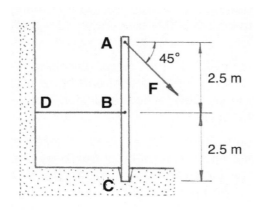

Pole ABC weighs 560 N. It is held in a vertical position by wire rope DB, and rests in a hole in the ground at point C. Force F = 3200 N is applied via another wire rope.

Determine the magnitude and direction of the force that the pole exerts on the ground at point C. (By the shape of the hole in the ground it should be evident that the ground cannot exert a moment on the pole, but only a horizontal and a vertical force.) [3617 N, W 47.10°S]

Question 11

A 180 kg lawn roller of diameter 400 mm is being pulled slowly along a path made of stone slabs, when it comes to a stop against a ridge formed by one slab standing proud of the previous one by 10 mm. Determine the magnitude of force P required to pull the roller over the ridge. Assume that the raised slab suffers no damage at point B, and that the frictional torque in the bearings of the roller is negligible.   [827.1 N]

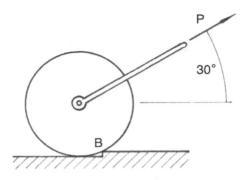

True/false questions to test your understanding of moments and equilibrium

1. A force moment has the same units as a torque.

2. For a rigid object in one plane to be in equilibrium, the only requirements are that $\Sigma F_x = 0$ and $\Sigma F_y = 0$.

3. An oblique force F applied at a point 'A' on an object, situated a distance 'd' from a pivot point 'O' on the object, such that the angle between the force and line OA is θ, has a moment about point 'O' equal to Fd cosθ.

4. If a rigid body is in equilibrium, the sum of the moments about all points on the body has to be zero.

5. For a rigid body in one plane that is in equilibrium, it is possible to solve for up to three unknown forces acting on the body.

6. A force couple consists of two equal and opposite forces with parallel lines of action.

7. A force couple has a rotational as well as a translational effect on a body.

8. A free-body diagram of an object should show all the forces acting on the object as well as all the forces that the object exerts on its surroundings.

9. A force whose line of action passes through a given point on a body can have no moment about that point.

10. The reactions at the supports of a beam are the forces that the beam exerts on its supports.

Conclusion

This chapter has defined force moments and torque, and has illustrated how these have to be taken into account to determine unknown forces, angles or dimensions for a solid object that is in equilibrium.

Most importantly, this chapter has demonstrated the technique for and the need for drawing a free-body diagram in order to solve for any unknowns in this type of circumstance.

This knowledge can now be applied to methods of determining the forces that arise in the members of structures and frames, which are demonstrated in Chapter 7. However, before going on to analyse structures, we need to have a solid grasp of the subject of centres of gravity. This topic is dealt with in Chapter 6, which follows.

Chapter 6

Centres of gravity, centres of mass and centroids

Definition of centres of gravity (CG) and centres of mass (CM), and their importance.

Rules for locating the CG of an object

General rule for locating the CG of masses arrayed in a straight line

Masses arrayed in 2-D

Dealing with masses, volumes and areas removed from a larger object

Centroids of areas and volumes

Masses arrayed in 3-D

Locating the CG of structures made of straight rods

Practical methods of determining the location of a CG of an irregularly shaped object

Determining the location of the CG of an object whose shape is described by a mathematical function

Definition of a centre of gravity and a centre of mass

Within the boundaries of every rigid body, a point can be found, through which the weight of the body seems to act.

If you pick up an irregularly shaped object, such as a household broom, it is possible to find a point on the handle where it is easiest to support the weight of the broom, and keep it balanced.

The net gravitational force on the broom must act through this point, because one could support the broom at this point with a single upward force that balances the weight of the broom. This point is called the **centre of gravity** of the object.

The centre of gravity of a rigid object does not change position within the object. Once you have established the location of that point, you can always support the weight of the

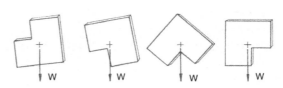

object by a single upward force whose line of action passes through this point, irrespective of the orientation of the object.

Centre of mass: It turns out that the point we call the centre of gravity is also *the same point* through which inertial forces act, when an object is being accelerated. In analysing situations where acceleration occurs, this point is referred to as the centre of mass.

If one needs to apply a force to impart linear acceleration or deceleration to an object, the force should be applied such that its line of action passes through the centre of mass of the object. Otherwise, the force will cause the object to rotate, as well as to change position.

Which term to use: It makes no difference whether one uses the term 'centre of mass', or 'centre of gravity', because both terms describe the same point in the space within the boundaries of a given rigid object. In this chapter we will refer to this point as the centre of gravity, abbreviated CG. We lean towards this usage because the method of determining the location of such a point relies on a consideration of gravitational forces in a situation of static equilibrium.

The importance of knowing the location of the CG of an object

Knowing the location of the centre of gravity of an object or assembly of objects is vital in applications like the following:

- Reducing the likelihood of a vehicle overturning when taking a curve in the road.
- Knowing where to attach support points on an object being raised by a crane.
- Maintaining the stability of a small boat when changing position in the boat.
- Placing the load correctly in a ship or aircraft.
- Determining the inertial forces on a moving machine part.
- Ensuring the stability of a suspended item like a pulley running on a rope.

Rules for locating the CG of an object

1. The location of the centre of gravity of a given rigid object is fixed and would only change if the object were to be deformed, or have material added or removed.

2. The location of a centre of mass/gravity depends on the way that the mass is distributed through the object. The CG is usually close to the largest concentration of mass present.

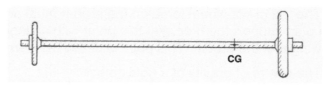

Consider a weightlifting bar of negligible mass, with a small mass-piece attached at one end, and a large one at the other. It is clear that there is not the same amount of mass on either side of the CG.

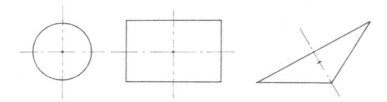

3. If an object has an axis of symmetry, the CG will be located on that axis.

4. If an object has two axes of symmetry, the CG lies at their intersection.

5. The CG of a given object always lies within the outer boundaries of the object, though not necessarily inside the material from which the object is made. For example, the CG of a horseshoe lies somewhere in the space between the arms of the shoe.

6. Some objects have regular geometric shapes. If they also have uniform density throughout, it is possible to determine the location of the CG of such objects mathematically.

7. If an object is irregular in shape, the location of its CG must be determined by one of the practical procedures explained further on.

Determining the location of the CG of a composite object by considering moments about a given point

We make use of the fact that the weight of the object, acting through its CG, has the same effect as the combined weights of the constituent parts of the object.

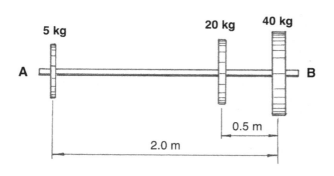

To illustrate this principle, consider an object similar to a weightlifting bar.

Shown is a 10 kg rod, on which some disc-shaped mass-pieces are fixed, as shown here:

By inspection, we can see that the CG of the assembly will be closer to end B of the rod than to end A.

To determine its exact position, we perform the following steps:

Make two drawings of the rod, positioned alongside one another.

On the left hand diagram we show, as force vectors, the individual weights of all the parts of the assembly. The weight of the rod, which is one of the parts of the assembly, acts through its midpoint, as the rod is of uniform section.

On the right-hand diagram we show the total weight of the assembly, acting through the CG of the assembly.

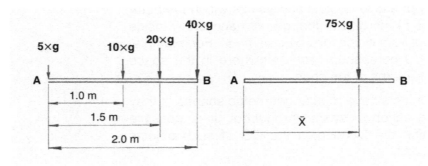

Let the distance from point A to the CG be labelled $\overline{X}$, pronounced 'x-bar'. This symbol is conventionally used to denote the distance from a reference point to a CG, in the x-direction.

If the two systems shown are equivalent, then the sum of the moments about point A of the individual weights must be equal to the moment about point A of the total weight.

ΣM_A of the individual weights........is equivalent to........ΣM_A of the total weight

$\therefore (10\text{ g} \times 1.0) + (20\text{ g} \times 1.5) + (40\text{ g} \times 2.0) = (75\text{ g} \times \overline{X})$

$\therefore (10 + 30 + 80)\text{g} = (75\,\overline{X})\text{g}$

Solving the above equation yields the value $\overline{X} = 1.6$ m

Note: The gravitational acceleration 'g' is a common factor to both sides of the above equation, and therefore the solution of this equation does not depend on the value of 'g'.

It follows that the location of the CG of a rigid body is independent of the value of 'g'. The CG would be in the same place on the body whether that body was on Earth, on Jupiter, or in outer space. This also means that in all future calculations, we can ignore the value of 'g' and work with the masses of all components, instead of their weights.

The method used in the example above is the basis of all the methods for determining the location of a CG of any assembly of parts, by calculation.

Exercise: Three disc-shaped mass-pieces are attached to a 2 kg rod in the positions shown.

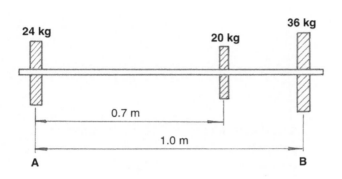

Determine the location of the CG of the assembly with respect to point A. [625 mm]

If the two end-pieces remain in place, where should the 20 kg mass-piece be fastened in order to ensure that the CG of the assembly is midway between A and B? [200 mm from A]

The general rule for locating the CG of masses arrayed in a straight line

Suppose we have a rod of negligible mass, on which is arranged a number of mass-pieces.

Let each one be an identifiable distance from the reference point 'A' at the left hand end of the rod.

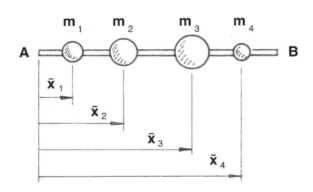

As before, the sum of the moments about point 'A' of the individual masses must be equal to the moment about point 'A' of the total mass. Hence, we can draw two equivalent diagrams:

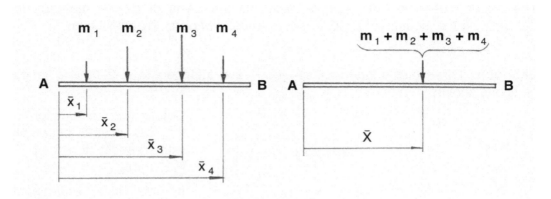

ΣM_A of the individual weights........is equivalent to........ΣM_A of the total weight

Therefore: $(m_1 \bar{x}_1 + m_2 \bar{x}_2 + m_3 \bar{x}_3 + m_4 \bar{x}_4) = (m_1 + m_2 + m_3 + m_4) \bar{X}$

$\therefore \bar{X} = (\Sigma m_i \bar{x}_i)/(\Sigma m_i)$ ....(1)

This is the general form of the equation that can be used to determine the location of any CG. If the constituent parts of an assembly are distributed in 2 dimensions, x and y, then an exactly similar reasoning leads to the location of the CG in the y-direction being obtained from

$\bar{Y} = (\Sigma m_i \bar{y}_i)/(\Sigma m_i)$

And likewise, in the z-direction, if the constituent parts are distributed in 3-dimensions:

$\bar{Z} = (\Sigma m_i \bar{z}_i)/(\Sigma m_i)$

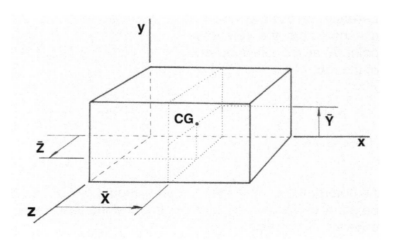

Locating the CG of mass-pieces arrayed in 2 dimensions

Example: Suppose three concentrated mass-pieces, P (10 kg), Q (12 kg) and R (15 kg), as shown here, are fixed to a rectangular board, S, of mass 2 kg.

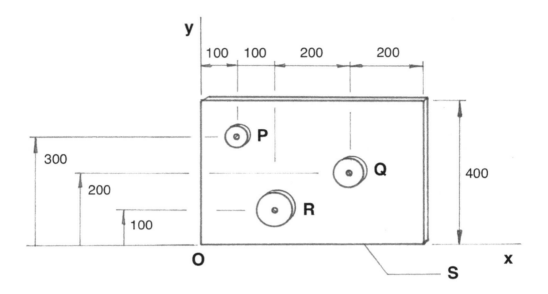

Determine the location of the CG of the assembly in relation to point 'O'.

Solution: It is convenient to construct a table to assist in organising the calculations. The mass of each component of the assembly must be listed alongside the dimensions that are relevant to it.

Part	mass m [kg]	x̄ [mm]	ȳ [mm]	mx̄ [kg.mm]	mȳ [kg.mm]
P	10	100	300	1000	3000
Q	12	400	200	4800	2400
R	15	200	100	3000	1500
S	2	300	200	600	400
Whole	39	n/a	n/a	9400	7300

$\bar{X} = (\Sigma m_i \bar{x}_i)/(\Sigma m_i)$: $\bar{X} = 9400$ kg.mm / 39 kg = 241.0 mm

$\bar{Y} = (\Sigma m_i \bar{y}_i)/(\Sigma m_i)$: $\bar{Y} = 7300$ kg.mm/ 39 kg = 187.2 mm

Exactly the same procedure can be used for assemblies in three dimensions, where we will need an extra two columns in the table, dealing with the variables that apply to the z-direction. For the moment, though, we will exercise this tabular method on a number of assemblies where the constituent parts are arranged in two dimensions.

Exercise: Determine the location of the CG of the following object, cut from a rectangular flat plate, of uniform thickness and density. These dimensions are all in cm.

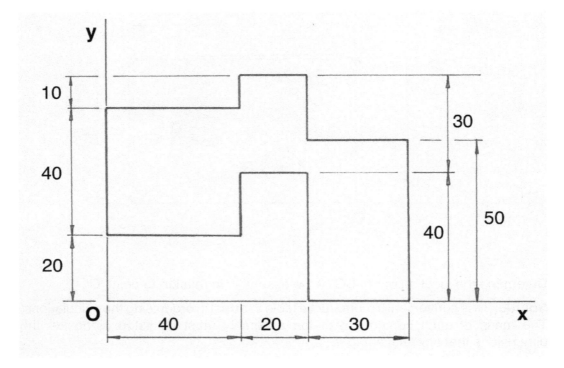

We can regard the plate as being made up of three small plates, P, Q and R, each of which is rectangular. The position of the CG of each of these plates is evident by inspection.

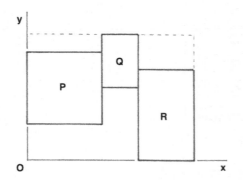

It is convenient to prepare a table, as in the preceding example, to assist with the calculations. Note: since the plates are all of uniform thickness and density, the area of each one is proportional to its mass. This enables us to replace masses with areas in the equation, and therefore in the table. The first row of data is given below. Complete the table from inspecting the diagram:

Part	Area 'a' [cm²]	x̄ [cm]	ȳ [cm]	x̄ a [cm³]	ȳ a [cm³]
P	1600	20	40	32000	64000
Q					
R					
Whole					

Since $\bar{X} = (\Sigma m_i \bar{x}_i)/(\Sigma m_i)$ and masses are proportional to areas:

$\bar{X} = (\Sigma \bar{x} a)/(\Sigma a)$ = ...[answer 47.16 cm]

and the same applies to the vertical direction:

$\bar{Y} = (\Sigma \bar{y} a)/(\Sigma a)$ = ...[answer 36.35 cm]

Dealing with masses, volumes and areas that have been *removed* from an assembly

Now consider what the effect on the location of the CG would be, if an area of the plate were to be removed, instead of added.

Proceed exactly as before, except that an area, mass or volume which is removed is considered as negative, and is given a negative sign in the table.

We can check on the reliability of this approach, by using the same plate that was given in the previous exercise.

Only, this time, consider the plate to consist of the large rectangle, C, that circumscribes the whole plate, minus four smaller rectangles, D, E, F, and G:

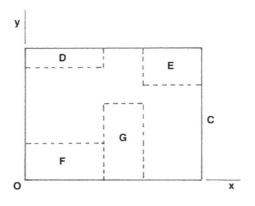

Draw up a similar table, and apply the same equations to the results. The answers ought to be identical with the ones obtained previously.

Part	Area 'a' [cm²]	$\bar{x}$ [cm]	$\bar{y}$ [cm]	$\bar{x}$ a [cm³]	$\bar{y}$ a [cm³]
C	6300	45	35	283500	220500
D	-400	20	65	-800	-26000
E					
F					
G					
Whole					

Exercise

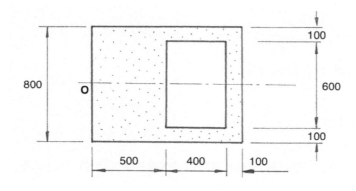

The plate illustrated here has a rectangular piece removed.

Determine the location of the CG of the plate, measured from point 'O'.

Consider this assembly to consist of the complete original plate, 'P', from which a smaller plate, 'Q', has been removed.

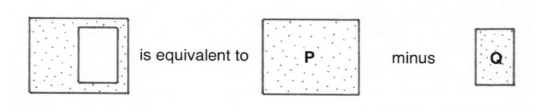

Construct the table, and perform the calculations as before.   [$\bar{X}$ = 414.3 mm]

Example

This example shows a practical application of considering a removed piece to be a negative area, volume, or mass. If the location of the CG of an assembly is already known, and a part of that assembly is now removed, we can determine how far the CG has become displaced.

Consider a motor-car wheel, diameter 660 mm, that was originally balanced by the addition of some small mass-pieces designed to be clipped onto the rim, at a radius of 180 mm. When balanced, the mass of the wheel was 15.47 kg, and the CG of the wheel was at the centre of rotation.

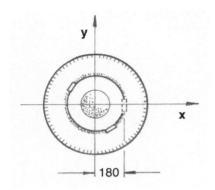

Now, if one of these balance weights, of mass 20 grams, has come off, how far has the CG become displaced from the centre of rotation?

Consider the assembly to be made up of the balanced wheel, minus the absent mass-piece.

The table to determine the location of the new CG now looks as follows (all dimensions are measured from the centre of rotation):

Part	mass m [kg]	$\bar{x}$ [m]	$\bar{x}$ m [m.kg]
Complete wheel when balanced	15.47	0	0
Missing mass-piece	−0.02	0.18	−0.0036
Whole assembly (unbalanced wheel)	15.45		−0.0036

$\bar{X} = (\Sigma m_i \bar{x} i)/(\Sigma mi)$, therefore $\bar{X} = (-0.0036)/(15.45) = -0.000233$ m $= -0.233$ mm

Why the minus sign: the dimensions in this table are *displacements*. There has to be a sign convention indicating the sense of any displacement in the x-direction. The dimension 0.18 m in the table was positive, so if the missing mass-piece was originally to the right of the axis of rotation, the new CG is 0.233 mm to the left of this axis.

One might think that the displacement of the CG by so small an amount was insignificant. However, while rotating, the wheel is now behaving as if it were a point mass of 15.45 kg situated 0.233 mm from the axis of rotation. At a vehicle speed of 120 km/h, the centrifugal force on this wheel would be approximately 36 N, rotating at approximately 16 times per second, sufficient to cause a noticeable wobble. Centrifugal force is explained in a subsequent chapter, in volume 3 of this series.

Centroids of areas and volumes

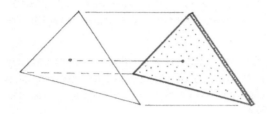

The centroid of a plane area is a point on its surface that corresponds with the CG which that surface would have, if it were a thin plate, of uniform thickness and density. (This type of thin plate is often referred to as a 'lamina'. This word comes directly from Latin, meaning a thin plate of marble or metal.)

The centroid of a volume is that point within the volume that corresponds with the CG of a solid object with uniform density, and the same shape as that volume.

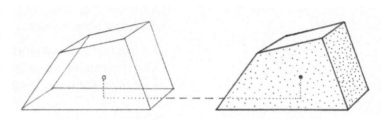

Standard expressions for the location of the centroids of various regular geometric areas and volumes
(derived by methods similar to that demonstrated at the end of this chapter.)

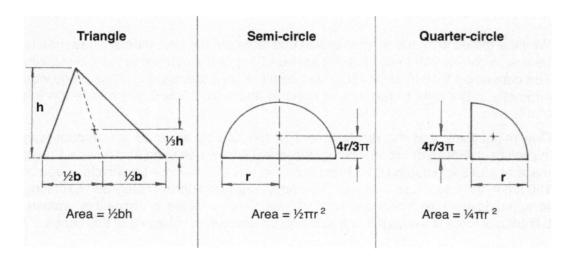

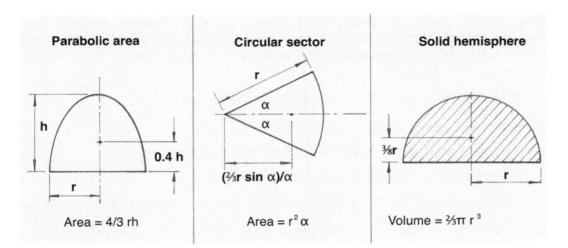

Parabolic area	Circular sector	Solid hemisphere

Parabolic area

h

0.4 h

r

Area = 4/3 rh

Circular sector

r

α
α

$(\tfrac{2}{3}r \sin \alpha)/\alpha$

Area = $r^2 \alpha$

Solid hemisphere

$\tfrac{3}{8}r$

r

Volume = $\tfrac{2}{3}\pi r^3$

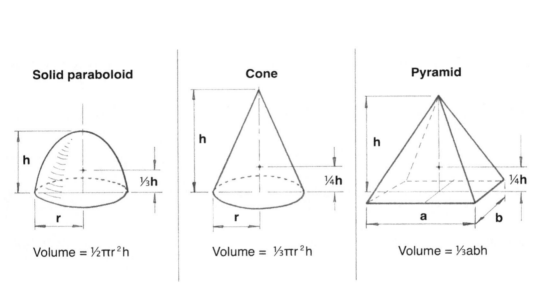

Solid paraboloid

h

$\tfrac{1}{3}h$

r

Volume = $\tfrac{1}{2}\pi r^2 h$

Cone

h

$\tfrac{1}{4}h$

r

Volume = $\tfrac{1}{3}\pi r^2 h$

Pyramid

h

$\tfrac{1}{4}h$

a

b

Volume = $\tfrac{1}{3}abh$

Example

The object illustrated here is turned from solid brass, density 8400 kg/m³, and can be thought of as a hollow hemisphere adjoining a hollow cylinder.

Determine the location of its CG above point 'O'.

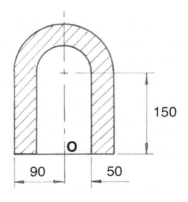

150

O

90   50

Since all the constituent 'parts' of this assembly are of the same material, their masses are proportional to their volumes. It will thus not be necessary to determine their masses, as we can work with volumes instead. The equation for determining $\bar{Y}$ becomes : $\bar{Y} = (\Sigma \bar{y}v)/(\Sigma v)$

Consider the assembly to be made up of four parts:

A. Solid hemisphere, r = 90 mm,

B. Removed solid hemisphere, r = 50 mm, hence negative volume

C. Solid cylinder, r = 90 mm and h = 150 mm

D. Removed solid cylinder, r = 50 mm and h = 150 mm, hence negative volume

Determine the volumes of the respective parts, and insert these values into the standard table. Note: the heights above the bases of the two solid hemispheres are added to the height of the cylinder, to give the $\bar{y}$ dimensions relative to the base of the assembly.

Confirm by your own calculations that the table should contain the following values:

Part	Volume, v [mm³]	$\bar{y}$ [mm]	$\bar{y}v$ [mm⁴] x 10⁶
A	1562814	183.75	287.167
B	−261799	168.75	−44.179
C	3817035	75	286.278
D	−1178097	75	−88.357
Whole	3939953		440.909

$\bar{Y} = (\Sigma \bar{y}v)/(\Sigma v) = 440.909 \times 10^6 / 3.939953 \times 10^6 = 111.9$ mm

Example of locating a CG in 3 dimensions

When locating a CG in 3-dimensions, the procedure is unchanged, except that the table requires two more columns, to accommodate calculations pertaining to the 'z' direction.

See the diagram on the following page, depicting a square raft, 'A', which is 6m x 6 m x 0.2 m thick, and of uniform section and density. The mass of this raft is 1800 kg. On this raft are placed two loads, 'B' and 'C', as shown. Load 'B' is a rectangular crate, with dimensions 1 m x 2 m x 2 m, and mass 800 kg. Load 'C' is a cubic crate, of side 1 m, with mass 2100 kg. Determine the location of the CG of the assembly, with respect to point 'O'. Assume that the CGs of the crates coincide with their centroids.

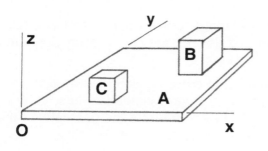
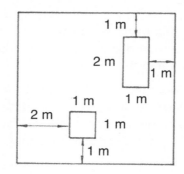

Part	x̄ [m]	ȳ [m]	z̄ [m]	m [kg]	x̄m [m.kg]	ȳm [m.kg]	z̄ m [m.kg]
A	3.0	3.0	−0.1	1800	5400	5400	−180
B	2.5	1.5	0.5	800	2000	1200	400
C	4.5	4.0	1.0	2100	9450	8400	2100
Whole				4700	16850	15000	2320

$\bar{X} = (\Sigma m_i \bar{x}_i)/(\Sigma m_i)$ ∴ $\bar{X} = 16850 /4700 = 3.585$ m

$\bar{Y} = (\Sigma m_i \bar{y}_i)/(\Sigma m_i)$ ∴ $\bar{Y} = 15000/4700 = 3.191$ m

$\bar{Z} = (\Sigma m_i \bar{z}_i)/(\Sigma m_i)$ ∴ $\bar{Z} = 2320/4700 = 0.494$ m

Exercise

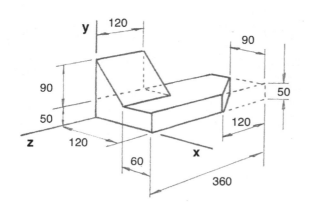

This item comprises a flat rectangular steel slab from which a triangular piece has been removed, and to which has been added a triangular prism of the same material.

Determine the location of its CG with respect to the axes indicated.

[$\bar{X}$ = 50.49 mm

$\bar{Y}$ = 33.05 mm

$\bar{Z}$ = −145.4 mm]

Locating the CG of structures made of straight rods

Such structures include roof trusses, bridge spans, crane booms, and electricity pylons. If the rods are of uniform section and density, the CG of each single rod lies at its own midpoint.

Also, if the rods are all of the same material and cross-section, their masses are proportional to their lengths, so we can work with lengths instead of masses. If we can determine the locations of each rod's individual CG from the geometry of the frame, we have the necessary $\bar{x}$ and $\bar{y}$ dimensions to complete our table.

Example:

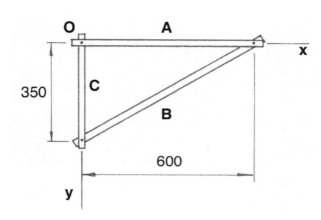

Determine the location of the CG of this assembly with respect to point 'O'. The assembly is made of three straight flat bars, identical in section. The mass of the bolts joining the bars may be ignored. The bars extend 20 mm beyond each joint.

Bars 'A' and 'C' are conveniently orientated in the x and y directions. However, bar 'B' is not. We need the location of the CG of bar 'B' before the table can be drawn up.

Length of bar 'B' between the bolts: by Pythagoras, $B^2 = A^2 + C^2$ hence $B = 694.6$ mm

The full length of bar 'B' is thus $694.6 + 2(20) = 734.6$ mm
Likewise, the full length of 'A' is 640 mm and that of 'C' is 390 mm

Part	length, L [mm]	$\bar{x}$ [mm]	$\bar{y}$ [mm]	$\bar{x}$ L [mm²]	$\bar{y}$ L [mm²]
A	640	300	0	192000	0
B	734.6	300	175	220380	128555
C	390	0	175	0	68250
Whole	1764.6			412380	196805

$\bar{X} = (\Sigma L_i \bar{x}_i)/(\Sigma L_i)$: $\therefore \bar{X} = 412380/1764.6 = 233.7$ mm

$\bar{Y} = (\Sigma L_i \bar{y}_i)/(\Sigma L_i)$: $\therefore \bar{Y} = 196805/1764.6 = 111.5$ mm

Practical methods of determining the location of a CG of an irregularly shaped object

If you need to establish the position of the CG of an irregularly shaped object that is not made up of recognisable geometric figures, there are three possible ways to do this. The method you choose depends on the size and shape of the object.

1. For objects made from flat plate

a. Suspend the object from one point, with a plumb-bob (small mass-piece on a thin flexible string) suspended from the same point.

b. Trace the plumb-bob line on the surface of the plate, in pencil. This is best done by making two pencil marks some distance apart, immediately under the string, and afterwards joining these two marks with a ruled line.

c. Repeat, with the object suspended from a different point.

d. The point where the two lines cross will be the CG.

e. The procedure can be repeated using any number of suspension points. All the traced lines will intersect at this same point.

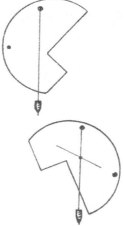

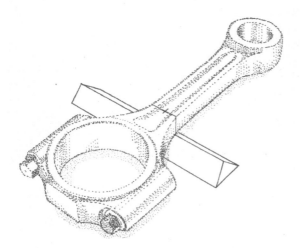

2. For objects that are light enough to be manhandled, and of more or less uniform thickness

a. Place the object across a knife-edged support, and position it by trial and error, until it is balanced.

b. The CG is located above the line of contact with the knife-edge.

3. For a long object that can be weighed at points near its extremities

a. Position the object horizontally, supported or suspended at two points, 'A' and 'B', a distance 'd' apart, such that a weight reading can be made at one or both of these points.

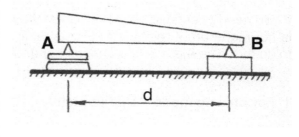

b. If only one weighing scale is available, switch the scale between the support points, ensuring that the object remains in the same horizontal position for both weighings.

Determine the value of $\overline{X}$ by the following method:

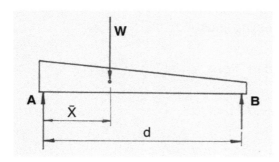

The total weight of the object, $W = A + B$

Consider moments about point A:

$W\overline{X} = B\,d,$

hence $\overline{X} = Bd/W$

Exercise

An aircraft is supported at two points, A and B, that are 6.38 m apart. The landing wheels rest on a weighing scale at point 'A', while a block, of the same height as the scale platform, is placed under the tail wheel at point 'B'.

The weight reading on the scale at A is 2180 kg. The block and the weighing scale are now switched around.

The weight reading at 'B' is 400 kg. Determine the horizontal distance, $\overline{X}$, from point A to the CG of the aircraft. [0.989 m]

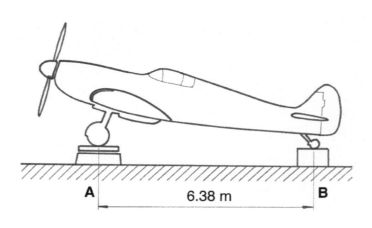

Exercises on centres of gravity

None of the exercises below is more 'difficult' in concept. Some of them are more complex because the objects in them consist of more parts, or because they need some calculations to be done before the table can be completed.

Question 1

The object shown here is made from four steel bars of uniform section, each 800 mm long, welded together. All the bars lie in the same plane. Determine the distance from the base to the CG of the assembly.

[300 mm]

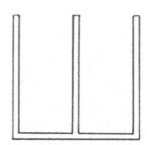

Question 2

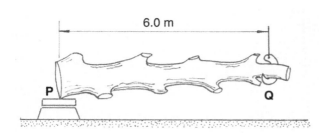

A tree-trunk is too heavy to be weighed on a weighing scale that registers up to 500 kg, so it is weighed separately at both ends.

When end 'P' is on the scale (while end 'Q' is supported), the scale reads 380 kg.

When the other end of the tree-trunk is on the scale, it reads 190 kg. Determine

* The mass of the tree-trunk ....[570 kg]
* The distance from end 'P' to the centre of gravity of the tree-trunk.......[2.00 m]

Question 3

The diagram shows a portion of a concrete dam wall, in section.

Determine the x- and y-co-ordinates of the centroid of this section. Consider the origin of the axes to coincide with the lower left corner.

[$\bar{X}$ = 16.33 m; $\bar{Y}$ = 13.33 m]

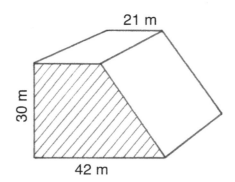

Question 4

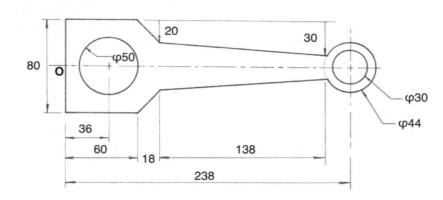

This machined object has a shape that is a rough approximation to that of a connecting rod.

The object has uniform thickness and density throughout.

Determine the distance from point O to its centre of mass, to the nearest mm. [101 mm]

Question 5

Three straight brass rods of the same cross-section are joined to form a right-angled triangle. Determine the location of the CG of this assembly.

[X̄ = 150 mm, Ȳ = 100 mm]

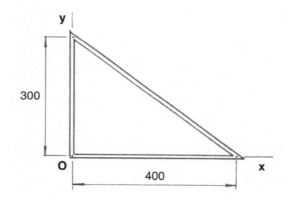

If the triangle had been a solid triangle, cut from plate of uniform thickness, what would have been the corresponding co-ordinates of the CG?

[X̄ = 133.3 mm, Ȳ = 100 mm]

Question 6

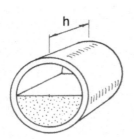

A hollow steel cylinder (relative density 7.7) contains a solid copper half-cylinder (relative density 8.9).

R = 180 mm, r = 160 mm, h = 250 mm.

How far below the upper flat surface of the copper is the CG of the assembly situated?   [46.5 mm]

Question 7

Consider this simplified car.

The diamond symbols show the location of the CG of each of the major mass concentrations that make up the vehicle.

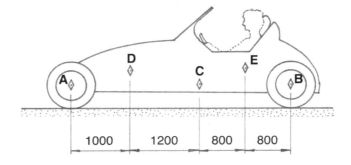

These masses are as follows:

A. Front wheel assembly .... 90 kg

B. Rear wheel assembly .... 60 kg

C. Chassis... ....320 kg

D. Engine .... 220 kg

E. Driver.. 80 kg

- Without a driver in the seat, how far is the CG from the front axle? [1.670 m]
- When an 80kg driver sits in the seat, what distance does the CG move? [138 mm towards the rear]
- With a driver in the seat, what is the percentage of the total weight carried by the front wheels? [52.4%]

Question 8

A 'fish' sculpture has to be suspended from a single wire rope so that it hangs horizontally, as shown. This sculpture consists of 3 plates: 'A', 'B', and 'C', all of solid steel, thickness 8 mm, welded to 3 pieces of 30 mm square-section solid steel bar, namely 'D', 'E' and 'F'. All the dimensions in the diagram are in centimetres.

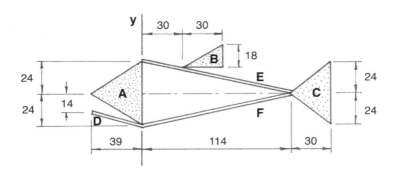

How far to the right of the given y-axis should the rope be attached?

[47.67 cm]

Question 12

A circular saw in a sawmill, with diameter 0.9 m, thickness 3 mm, carries 85 tungsten carbide teeth, each of mass 40 grams. The hole at the hub of the blade has a diameter of 60 mm.

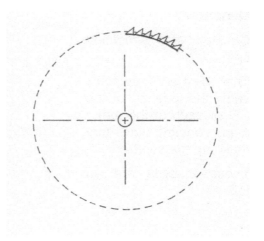

If one of the teeth breaks off during operation, by what margin is the CG of the blade now off-centre? Take the relative density of the steel of which the blade is made to be 7.8. [0.99 mm]

This dimension may seem very small, but the centrifugal force due to an off-centre rotating mass can give rise to a significantly powerful rotary vibration at the high speeds at which a saw blade normally operates.

To give a perspective on the significance of such an apparently minor loss of centricity, the centrifugal force calculation shows that if this saw operated at 2000 r/min, the centrifugal force caused by this saw blade's mass rotating at 0.99 mm from its axis of rotation would be around 790 N (equivalent to the weight of a full-grown man). All on account of one 40 gram tooth coming off! This example illustrates the need for rotating machinery to be thoroughly balanced.

Determining the location of the CG of an object whose shape is described by a mathematical function.

Previously in this chapter, several expressions were provided, showing the x- or y-co-ordinate of the centroid of different regular geometric plane and solid figures.

At the point at which they were introduced, expressions of this sort were simply provided, but their derivation was not shown. Such expressions can be derived by a process of integration. For the sake of example, and to demonstrate the reliability of the given expressions, one such derivation is shown below.

This method can be used on all areas whose boundaries are determined by algebraic functions. The same method can be extended to 3-D objects whose surfaces can be described by algebraic functions. However, the likelihood that the average engineer would ever need to do this is minimal.

Determining the location of the centroid of a semicircular plane area

The process makes use of the same principle we have used in all our calculations to determine the location of a centroid, to date: namely, that the sum of the moments of the constituent areas about some point 'O' must equal the moment of the whole area about point 'O'.

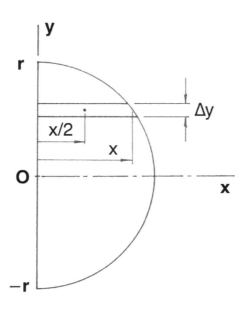

Consider the semicircular area, with radius 'r', shown here. One horizontal element is illustrated. The figure may be considered to consist of a number of these elements.

The height of each strip is Δy, and the length of it is x. The centroid of the strip is located a distance (x/2) from the y-axis.

The moment of the area of this strip about the y-axis is given by:

(area) $\times$ (distance to centroid) namely $(x \Delta y)(x/2)$ or $(x^2/2)\Delta y$.

In the limit, as Δy is made smaller, it becomes dy.

The sum of the moments of all such strips between the y-values of (−r) and (+r) may be found by the integration:

$$\Sigma M_y = \int_{-r}^{r}(x^2/2)\ dy$$

The equation of the circle is $x^2 = r^2 - y^2$, so, substituting for x^2 into the above integral, it becomes:

$$\Sigma M_y = \tfrac{1}{2}\int_{-r}^{r}(r^2 - y^2)\ dy = \tfrac{1}{2}(r^2 y]_{-r}^{r} - \tfrac{1}{2}(y^3/3]_{-r}^{r}$$

$$= r^3 - r^3/3 = \tfrac{2}{3} r^3$$

This represents the sum of the moments of the areas of all the elements about the y-axis, which sum must equal the moment of the *entire* area about the y-axis, which is (entire area) × (moment arm), namely $(\frac{1}{2}\pi\, r^2)\, \overline{X}$

$$\therefore\ \tfrac{2}{3}\, r^3 = (\tfrac{1}{2}\pi r^2)\, \overline{X} \qquad \therefore\ \overline{X} = 4r/3\pi$$

A practical experiment to verify the tabular procedure for determining the location of the CG of a lamina.

An ideal material for the lamina would be a sheet of pegboard, which is suitable due to the even distribution of holes in it. Boards may be suspended from any existing hole in the material without having to make a new hole, which would remove material.

The idea is to make a composite shape, locate its CG by the method of suspending it together with a plumb-bob, and also make the parts that comprise the composite shape, and do likewise for each of them.

Then apply the tabular method to the group of individual parts that make up the whole, to determine by calculation $\overline{X}$ and $\overline{Y}$ for the whole lamina, and compare the answers with the $\overline{X}$ and $\overline{Y}$ values obtained by suspending the composite shape.

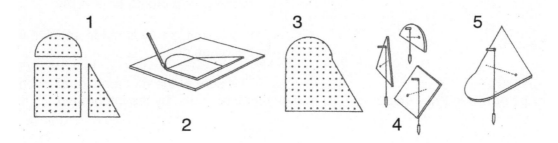

It is advisable to make the component parts first, to eliminate the loss of material that would arise from the width of a saw cut if two identical composite shapes were made and one of them were to be cut into component parts.

Make the small shapes as precisely as possible, then group them together tightly, taped together, on top of a sheet of the same material, mark the outline and cut it.

In classes run by the author, typically, for composite shapes that are approximately 300 mm across, the values found by the tabular method agreed with those found by suspending the composite shape, to within less than 1 mm. This has been found to be the case with various combinations of shapes, including arrangements that have negative shapes as components.

True/False questions

To test your knowledge of centres of gravity and centroids

1. The location of the CG of a solid object can be altered by deforming the object.

2. In some circumstances, the locations of the centre of gravity, and the centre of mass of a rigid body could differ.

3. It is possible for the CG of a rigid body to lie outside the boundary of the extremities of that body.

4. If there is an axis of symmetry on a rigid body, the CG always lies on that axis.

5. If a rigid body is placed with is base upon a flat horizontal surface, and it topples, that means its centre of mass is located outside the boundaries of the base of the object.

6. The location of the centroid of a regularly-shaped plane area can be found by a method involving integration.

7. The essential method of determining the location of a CG consists of equating two sets of equivalent moments about a given point.

8. When using the tabular method to determine the location of a CG of a composite body, parts that are 'removed' may be considered to have negative mass.

9. When determining the location of a CG by calculation, if the answer turns out to be negative, there must have been an error in the calculations.

10. If the method of two weighings is used to locate the CG of an irregularly shaped object, it makes no difference how far apart the support points are chosen.

11. There is always the same amount of mass on either side of the centre of mass of a rigid body, from whichever angle it is viewed.

12. To determine the height above the base of a truncated cone to its CG, it is necessary first to know the dimensions of the full cone, before it was truncated.

Chapter 7

Forces in structures: trusses and frames

Definitions of a truss and a frame

Trusses are structures made up of an open lattice-work (known also as a 'web') of members that are straight sections of material, joined at their ends. Such structures occur in roof trusses, bridges, crane jibs, crane booms, and electricity pylons.

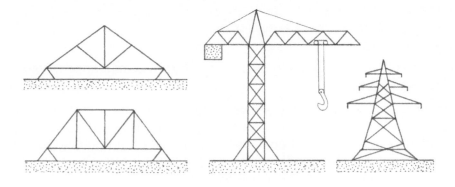

In a true truss, all the members are straight, joined only at their ends, in such a way as not to constrain members from rotating relative to one another, and all external loads are applied only at the nodes (joints). Each member can experience either tension or compression, but not bending.

Frames are similar to trusses, except that one (or more) members of a frame extends beyond a node, so that such members can experience bending and shear in addition to tension or compression.

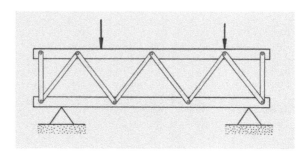

An example of a frame: one or more members extend beyond two nodes, and forces may be applied between nodes.

The material used for trusses and frames in large structures is usually steel, although other materials can be used, and the members can have any type of cross-section.

Many older railway bridges were supported by timber trusses. Modern roofs still make use of timber trusses, where the spans are not too large. For smaller structures, as in machinery, aluminium or other alloys are sometimes used.

Definition of a 'pin-jointed' truss

In the first part of this chapter we will consider only the simple case of two dimensional trusses, namely, those whose members lie in the plane of the paper, and are held together by 'pins' at the nodes. Later we extend the analysis to three dimensional trusses.

A pin, for the purposes of this analysis, is like a bolt that has not been fully tightened, or a rivet whose ends have not been hammered completely against the materials that it joins. A pin keeps the ends of the members together, but does not constrain them from rotating relative to one another.

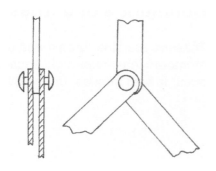

A truss that consists only of members joined at their ends by pins is easily analysed by the methods of static equilibrium.

A frame, on the other hand, can only be analysed by these methods if it is sufficiently simple and simply loaded.

Most frames are only able to be analysed by finite element methods, involving specialist computer programmes. We will not need to go to that level of specialisation: in the present chapter the reader will be introduced to the basic approaches to determining the forces in pin-jointed trusses. Such knowledge is essential preparation for eventual specialisation.

Over-constrained structures

If a rigid body or an assembly of rigid bodies in one plane is in static equilibrium, and has up to three unknown forces acting on it, the equations of equilibrium can be applied to determine the values of those unknown forces. Such an an object or assembly of objects is described as *statically determinate.*

However, if there are too many unknown forces present for us to solve using the three equations of equilibrium, then the structure is called *over-constrained*. A two-dimensional structure will be over-constrained when there are:

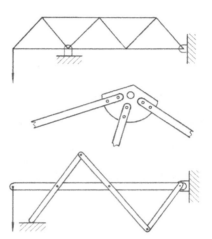

a. More than three unknown external forces (including reaction forces) acting on the structure, whether truss or frame.

b. Rigid joints that can transmit a force moment. (Found only in frames.)

c. Members extending through one or more nodes. (Found only in frames.)

Over-constrained structures are too complex to be analysed by the methods of static equilibrium, and will not be dealt with in this book.

Forces in the members of pin-jointed trusses

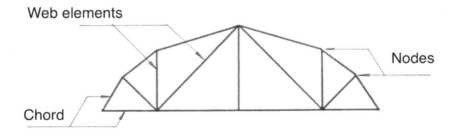

Members forming the outer envelope of the truss are collectively called the 'chord',
while those that span the space inside the chord are called 'web elements'.

When a pin-jointed truss is under load, each of the members experiences a unique loading. Any given member could be in tension, in compression, or carry no load. A member in tension is called a 'tie' and one in compression is called a 'strut'. If a member carries no load, it is called a 'no-load member'.

If a member is a 'tie' under a given loading, it need not be a solid member, because it will function just as well if it were replaced by a rope or chain.

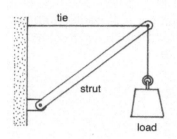

When designing a truss for a particular purpose, we need to determine the forces in each member of the truss, to ensure that a given external load pattern does not result in an unduly large force that could cause the failure of any member. Members experiencing excessive tension could snap, while those subjected to compression could be at risk of buckling or crushing. Pins subjected to too great a shear force could fail in shear.

A pin-jointed truss that has not collapsed may exhibit an overall deflection or 'bend' when under load. However, even if the chord (sometimes called the envelope) of the truss 'bends', the individual members do not bend. They can only lengthen or shorten marginally, due to tension or compression respectively. Any deflection of the chord is partly due to these very minor changes in length of the individual elements, and partly due to the play that exists in the joints. See more about this, further on.

Triangular stability

The illustration below shows a stable truss and an unstable truss. It is easy to see why frames and trusses are made up mostly of triangular divisions.

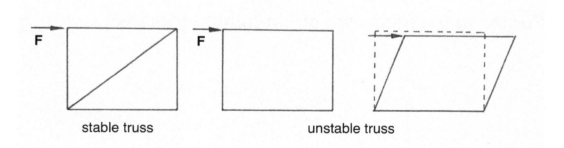

stable truss   unstable truss

However, it is not essential for all the spaces in a truss to be triangular.

For example, the truss shown here is stable, despite containing a quadrilateral space.

This truss is made stable by the triangular spaces, so that nodes 1 and 3 are firmly held in place.

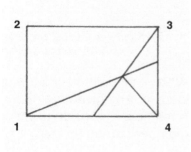

Some standard bridge-span trusses in common use

These trusses each have particular advantages, according to the materials from which they are made and the type of loading they are going to experience in use. Steel is prone to buckling when used in compression, so, if steel is used, designs with short compression members have an advantage. Truss bridges came into use in the 1820s and are still built for particular applications, particularly in areas to which relatively light bridge components need to be transported. Their construction is relatively simple, but they require high maintenance.

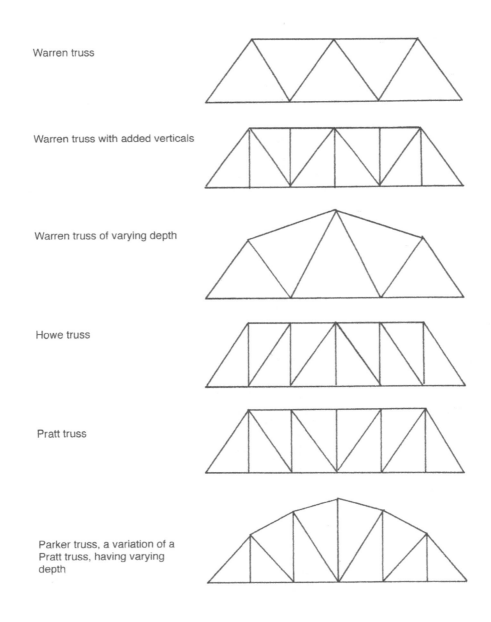

Warren truss

Warren truss with added verticals

Warren truss of varying depth

Howe truss

Pratt truss

Parker truss, a variation of a Pratt truss, having varying depth

Determining, by inspection, whether a member will be a strut or a tie

Trusses are mostly made up of triangular arrangements of members, for reasons of stability. If a space in a truss is bounded by more than three sides, there is a possibility that it will be unstable. If you apply a given loading to a four-sided pin-jointed truss, it is easy to predict which way the figure will go 'out of shape'.

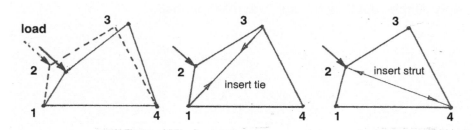

If you can see that joints 1 and 3 would move further apart as a result of the loading, you can insert a tie between node 1 and node 3 to keep the truss stable. Placing a strut between node 2 and node 4 would have the same effect.

Now consider this idea in reverse. If you start with a loaded truss that is stable because it consists of triangular spaces, consider what would happen to the truss if a particular member were to be *removed*. Would the two pin-joints to which that member had been attached move *apart* under the given loading, or would they move *closer*? If they would move apart, then the member is a tie. If they would move closer, the member is a strut.

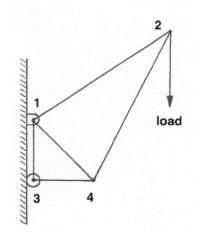

For example, consider the wall-crane truss shown here:

Under the given loading, if one were to remove the member 1 - 2, the joints at node 1 and node 2 would move further apart, so the member between these joints must be a tie.

Likewise, if the member 2 - 4 were to be removed, the joints at node 2 and node 4 would move closer together, so the member 2 - 4 has to be a strut.

However, what about member 1 - 3? It is not immediately apparent whether the nodes to which that member is attached would move closer together, or further apart.

No-load members: In some cases a member might appear, on inspection, to be a tie or a strut, but analysis will show that it is actually a 'no-load' member. A member that appears to carry no load might not look as if it contributes to the stability of a truss, but it is not there purely for decoration: it has a function, because as soon as the envelope of the truss distorts slightly under load, the member in question will carry *some* load.

It is not always easy to detect by inspection which members might be no-load members.

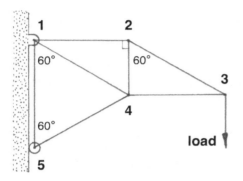

For instance, in this simple wall-crane, member 1 - 4 appears to be a strut, for, if it were to be removed, node 4 might be expected to move closer to node 1.

However, as will be seen from the analysis of this truss further on, member 1 - 4 is actually a 'no-load' member in this arrangement, under the given external loading. This simply means that with the given loading, the other members appear to be stable without the inclusion of member 1 - 4.

Three methods of determining the forces in the individual members of a pin-jointed truss.

The first step is always to determine the values of all the external forces (including the reactions at the supports) acting on the truss. Once this has been done, any of the following three methods can be used. These methods are all explained, in detail, in the pages that follow.

1. **Considering the equilibrium of each node**. Draw a FBD of each pin, assume the pin is in equilibrium, and solve for the unknown forces that the adjacent members must be exerting on that pin, using the equations for the equilibrium of the pin, namely $\Sigma F_x = 0$ and $\Sigma F_y = 0$.

2. **The 'method of sections'**, in which imaginary cuts or 'sections' are made through the truss at selected positions. The portion of the truss on one side of the 'section' can be regarded as a flat plate in equilibrium. This allows the equations $\Sigma F_x = 0$; $\Sigma F_y = 0$ and $\Sigma M_o = 0$ to be applied, to solve for the forces exerted on the 'plate' by adjacent members.

3. **Drawing a Maxwell diagram, using Bow's notation.** This is is a graphical method enabling the forces in all members to be determined by drawing, to scale, a combined force polygon for all the joints in the truss. The magnitudes and directions of the forces in the respective members are measured to scale directly from the diagram. In this method, after the initial determination of the values of the external forces acting on the truss, no further calculations are required.

We will apply all three methods to *the same* simple example, to demonstrate their use.

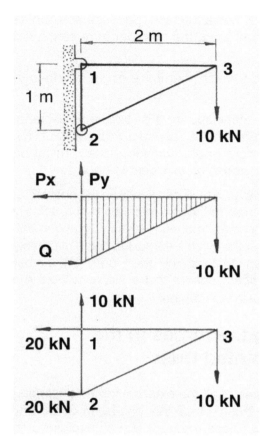

Shown here is a simple wall-crane carrying a load of 10 kN.

Allocate an identifying numeral to each node.

Then, determine the magnitudes of the external forces acting on the truss. In this example, we will ignore the weight of the truss, for simplicity.

Consider the whole truss as if it were a flat plate in equilibrium under the action of the external forces.

$\Sigma F_y = 0$, $\therefore P_y = 10$ kN

$\Sigma M_1 = 0$ $\therefore$ 10 kN $\times$ 2 m = Q $\times$ 1 m

$\therefore Q = 20$ kN

$\Sigma F_x = 0$ $\therefore P_x = 20$ kN

Hence the external forces acting on the truss are as shown here.

The force in the member joining nodes 1 and 2 will be named $F_{1\text{-}2}$, and so on.

Method 1: Considering the equilibrium of each individual node

a. Choose any pin that has at least one known force and a maximum of two unknown forces acting on it. We can only solve for two unknowns in each case, since the pin may be considered as a particle, for which no rotation is possible, so that a moment equation cannot be applied.

b. Draw the FBD of the pin, and apply $\Sigma F_x = 0$ and $\Sigma F_y = 0$ to solve for the unknowns.

c. Apply the same procedure to enough pins in the frame to enable a solution to be found for all the unknown forces.

It is convenient to begin with the pin at node1.

The FBD of the pin at node 1:

$\Sigma F_x = 0$, $\therefore F_{1\text{-}3} = 20$ kN

$\Sigma F_y = 0$, $\therefore F_{1\text{-}2} = 10$ kN

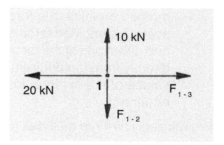

140

Member 1 - 2 pulls on the pin at node 1, therefore this member is in tension, and it follows that it also pulls on pin 2 with a force of 10 kN. We carry this fact over to our analysis of the forces acting on pin 2:

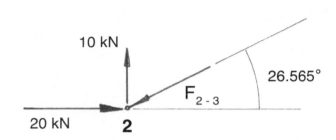

$\Sigma F_x = 0$

$\therefore F_{2-3} \cos 26.565° = 20$ kN

$\therefore F_{2-3} = 22.36$ kN

(check: $F_{2-3} \sin 26.565°$ should equal 10 kN)

We have now solved for all three of the unknown forces in the members of the frame. As a check on our results, we should move to the third node of the frame, and see if our answers are consistent with the equilibrium of the pin at that node.

The FBD of the pin at node 3:

$\Sigma F_x = 22.36 \cos 26.565° - 20$

which equals 0

$\Sigma F_y = 22.36 \sin 26.565° - 10$

which equals 0

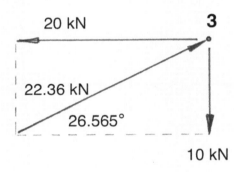

The above result confirms that the pin at node 3 is also in equilibrium, satisfying us that the values found for the forces in the respective members of the truss must be correct. These forces can now be represented in a diagram, as follows:

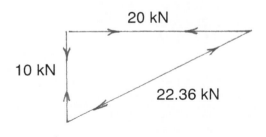

Method 2: The method of sections

a. Make an imaginary cut or 'section' through the truss at some convenient position. It is advisable to make the cut pass through 3 or fewer members in which the forces are not yet known.

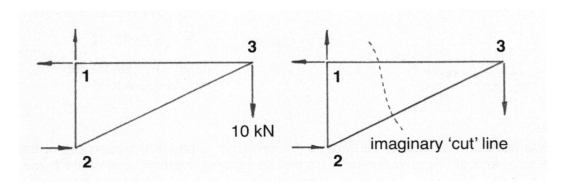

b. The portion of the truss to the left of the cut may be considered as a flat plate in equilibrium, so the three equations of equilibrium will apply to that 'plate'.

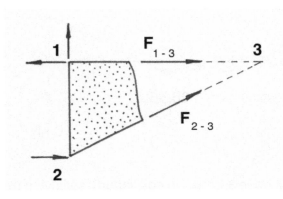

c. The magnitudes of the forces in the 'cut' members are unknown. However, these forces must be aligned with the members that have been 'cut'.

d. If unsure whether these forces push or pull on the 'plate', assume a direction for each of them. It is not important to be correct about this assumption, as an incorrect assumption will be revealed by the value turning out to be negative.

e. Solve for up to three unknowns by applying the equations of equilibrium to this 'plate'. The plate is a rigid body, not a single point, and for it to be in equilibrium, the moments about any point on the plate should sum to zero.

For convenience, to minimise the number of moments that need to be considered, choose a point through which most of the forces pass (except the one whose value you need to determine). $\Sigma M_1 = 0$

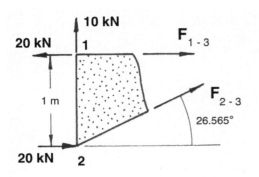

$\therefore (20 \times 1) + (F_{2 \cdot 3} \times 1.\cos 26.565°) = 0$

$\therefore F_{2 \cdot 3} = -22.36$ kN   (namely 22.36 kN opposite to the assumed sense)

To continue solving for unknown forces, take moments about a different point on the 'plate'. Say, node 2. Then $\Sigma M_2 = 0$

$\therefore (F_{1 \cdot 3} \times 1) = (20 \times 1) \therefore F_{1 \cdot 3} = 20$ kN

Check the validity of these values by using the values already found, to see whether a third condition of equilibrium for the cut 'plate' has been met:

Checking: $\Sigma F_x = 20 + 20 - 20 - 22.36 \cos 26.565° = 0$, thus confirming our answers.

If a truss is sufficiently complex, it may be necessary to make several 'sections' in this way, to determine the values of all the unknown forces in a truss.

Method 3: Drawing a Maxwell diagram, using Bow's notation

The physicist James Clerk Maxwell observed in the 1870s that there must be a direct correspondence between the shape of the force polygon that arises at each pin joint and the layout of the truss members that converge at that point. This has to be true, because, by the definition of a pin-jointed truss, the force in any member can only be either compressive or tensile, and therefore must have the same orientation as the member itself.

A Maxwell diagram is a graphical construction that combines in one diagram the force polygons for *all* the pin joints in a frame. Constructing this diagram is made easy by using the notation developed, also in the 1870s, by Robert Henry Bow, a Scottish civil engineer.

This method allows a graphical solution to be found for the magnitudes and directions of the forces in all the members, without performing any calculations. (Excepting, of course, those needed initially to determine the values of the external forces acting on the truss.)

Before drawing the Maxwell diagram, a scale drawing has to be made of the truss, and all external forces acting on the truss must be shown on this drawing, and labelled with their magnitudes.

This diagram is exactly the same as the one that resulted from our earlier determination of the external forces acting on the truss.

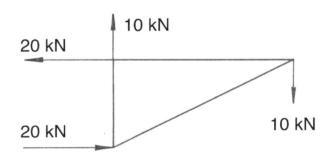

143

Bow's notation is applied as follows: On the drawing of the truss, assign a capital letter label to each space between any two adjacent forces. This applies to the spaces inside the truss, as well as those around the outside of the truss, which are separated by external forces.

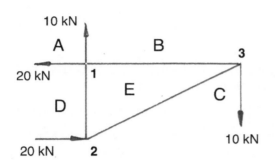

These capital letter labels will be used to guide us in naming the lines on the subsequent Maxwell diagram.

The Maxwell diagram will be a force diagram *without* any arrow-heads that are customarily used to denote the direction of forces.

The direction of all the forces on the diagram will be denoted by the sequence of letters that appear at the junctions of the force lines.

Each force on the diagram is named as follows: going *clockwise* around the pin joint, if a force lies between space A and space B, it is called 'a - b', in lower-case letters.

To construct the Maxwell diagram, begin with the forces acting at one of the pin joints at which at least one *known* external force acts, and at which no more than two unknown forces act. In the present example, it is convenient to start with node 1, since there are two known forces applied at this node.

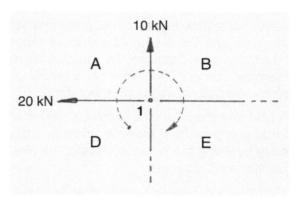

Draw a line representing one of the known forces, in magnitude and direction, to scale.

Begin with the 20 kN force separating space 'D' and space 'A'.

This force is directed from right to left, so the line 'd - a' on the Maxwell diagram runs from right to left.

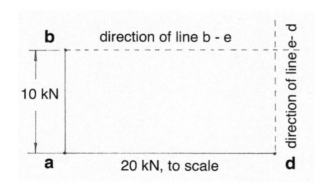

Now add line 'a - b' to the diagram.

The point 'a' on the diagram is common to lines 'd - a' and 'a - b'.

To fill in the lines for the unknown forces 'b - e' and 'e - d', note their direction, and draw in construction lines passing through the known points 'b' and 'd'. Point 'e' will be found where these extended lines intersect.

Now proceed to any one of the pin-joints adjacent to the one you have just processed. As before, read off the capital letters denoting the spaces, as you move clockwise around the joint. When all the nodes have been processed, the Maxwell diagram is complete. Now the magnitudes and directions of the forces in each member can read off the diagram, to scale.

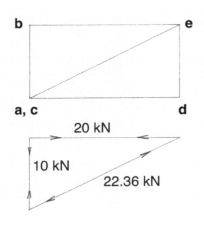

For example, the force in member BE (keep in mind that the sequence of these letters is *clockwise* about each node) is represented to scale, in both magnitude and direction, by the line 'b - e' on the Maxwell diagram. The force in member EB (at node 3) is represented by the line 'e - b'.

We can now fill in the tensions and compressions present in the respective members, on a diagram of the truss, and they will be identical (allowing for the accuracy of our scale drawing) with those found by the two methods used previously.

There is no need to be concerned that a graphical method may yield 'inaccurate' answers. If you draw the diagram carefully, you are bound to obtain results that are within 2% of the answers yielded by calculation methods. When one considers that, in choosing the materials for the truss members, a factor of safety is usually applied to make sure that members in a truss are at least twice as strong as they need to be, this 2% difference becomes negligible.

Exercise

The following 2-dimensional truss forms a simple crane. The load carried is 10 kN.

Determine the magnitudes and directions of the reactions at the supports, and determine the forces in each member of the crane, using all three methods described above, to verify your answers.

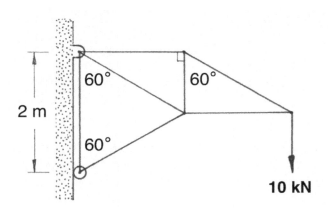

Solution:

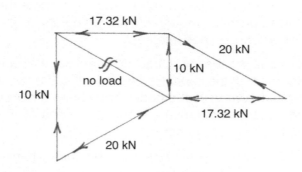

Identifying 'no-load' members

When a single member joins up with two other members that lie in a straight line, forming a T-junction, this member will carry no load. (Provided there is no external force acting on the pin at that joint.)

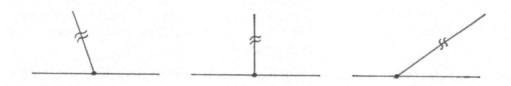

The reason that such a member carries no load, is that the forces acting on the pin have to be in equilibrium. Consider the two force diagrams below: If forces 'A' and 'B' lie in the same straight line, then their resultant cannot have a component at right angles to this line.

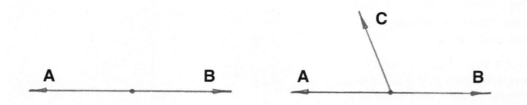

If a third force, 'C', pushes or pulls on the joint, it introduces a component at right angles to the line of action of forces 'A' and 'B'. This component cannot be balanced by the resultant of 'A' and 'B'. Consequently, the only condition that will satisfy equilibrium, is that 'A' and 'B' must be equal and opposite, and 'C' must have the value of zero.

If any other member joins this pin, or if an additional external force is applied at this pin, there is no longer a T-junction, and it is likely that all the forces converging at that pin will have non-zero values.

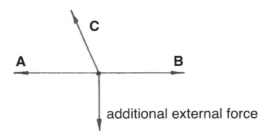

additional external force

We can therefore identify no-load members simply by discovering the T-junctions in a truss.

For example, consider the two roof-trusses shown here, both with the same given load-pattern:

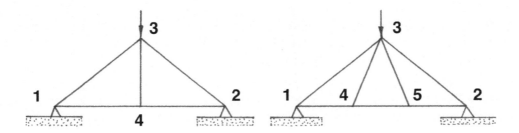

In the first one, member 3 - 4 will carry no load. In the second one, members 3 - 4 and 3 - 5 also carry no load. The forces in these trusses are exactly the same as in a simple triangular truss. Only the outer members of these two trusses carry load.

In the following two trusses, identify by inspection which members will carry no load:

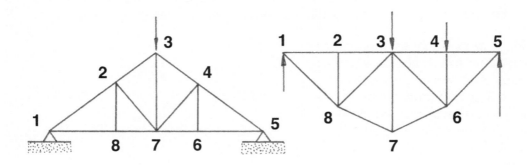

If a member in a truss carries no load, why is that member included? There are two reasons:

1. It is possible that, under a different loading, an external force could be applied to the pin-joint at the T-junction, rendering it no longer a T-junction.

147

2. The 'no-load' member is put there to stabilise other members. Long, slender struts are vulnerable to buckling. By dividing long struts into several shorter ones, and attaching these shorter sections to other members, the likelihood of buckling can be diminished. For example:

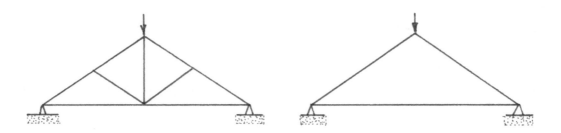

The truss on the left will have an identical load distribution to that on the right, but the one on the left supports what would have been long struts, in the middle of their spans, lessening the chance of them buckling.

In reality, pin-jointed trusses under load cannot hold their designated shape perfectly. The shape of the chord and the exact orientations of the web elements become slightly altered under load, for the following reasons:

1. Members will become slightly compressed or extended by the forces in them.

2. Members have significant mass, which adds to the loading that the truss experiences. In the present chapter we are ignoring the mass of the members.

3. In a proper pin-jointed truss, small amounts of play in the pin-joints would allow the truss to sag. Struts push on the pins at their ends, taking up any slack in the joint, effectively making the distance between pins even shorter than would result from compression. Likewise, the distance between the ends of a tie becomes greater than would be caused by the stretch due to tension.

So, a truss such as the one illustrated at left above, when under load, will end up looking more like this: (deflections exaggerated here), thus eliminating all T-junctions. This results in all the 'no-load' members carrying some load, even if the value of that load is small.

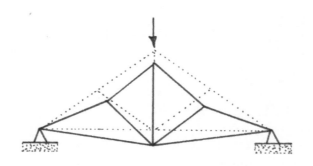

For the purposes of the types of analysis explained in the present chapter, we will not consider deflections in the envelope of a truss. All trusses will be presumed to retain their shapes.

Exercises on pin-jointed trusses

Question 1

A short bridge span is in the form of a Warren truss. All the members are 3 m long. With the given loading, determine the force in each of the respective members, assuming the structure is a properly pin-jointed truss.

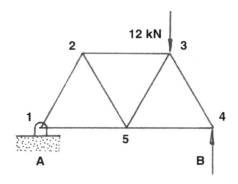

[Member 1-2 (strut): 3.464 kN; member 2-3 (strut): 3.464 kN ; member 3-4 (strut): 10.39 kN ; member 4-5 (tie): 5.196 kN ; member 5-1 (tie): 1.732 kN ; member 2-5 (strut): 3.464 kN; member 3-5 (strut): 3.464 kN]

Question 2

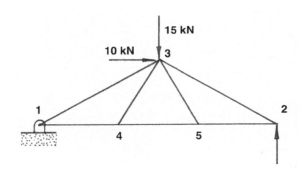

The pin-jointed roof truss shown here is supported by a hinge at joint 1 and a vertical force at joint 2, and carries loading as indicated. The five short members are each 3 m long.

Determine the magnitude of the greatest tension in any member, and the greatest compression in any member.

[Max. tension = 17.47 kN in all the horizontal members; max. compression = 20.32 kN in member 2 - 3]

Question 3

Compare the two wall-cranes shown here, both carrying the same load of 40 kN.

Determine the reactions at the supports and the forces in the members, and decide which of the two designs is the more practical.

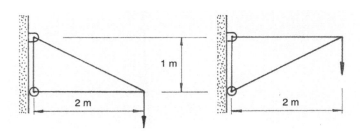

149

[Forces in members are 40 kN, 80 kN and 89.44 kN respectively, for both arrangements. The first arrangement is preferable, because, in the second arrangement, the largest compression force occurs in the longest member, increasing the risk of that member buckling.]

Question 4

This triangular truss carries one angled load. Determine the reactions at the supports, and draw a Maxwell diagram for the given loading, using Bow's notation. From this diagram, deduce the magnitude and nature of the forces in the respective members.

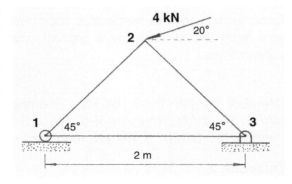

Solution:

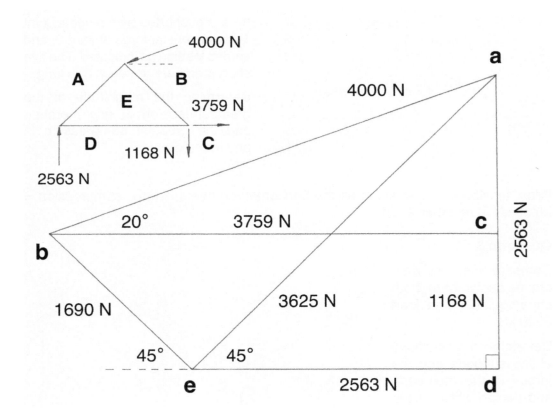

Member 1 - 2: strut, carrying 3625 N; Member 2 - 3: tie, carrying 1690 N;

Member 3 - 1: tie, carrying 2563 N

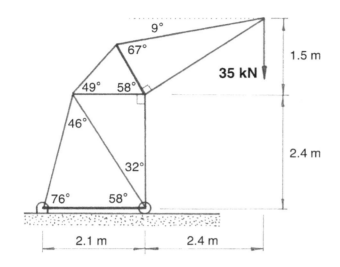

Question 5.

The simple crane shown here carries a load of 35 kN.

Consider the structure to be a pin-jointed truss, stable in the plane of the paper.

Determine the reactions at the supports, and draw a Maxwell diagram to determine the magnitudes and directions of the forces in all the members.

Solution:

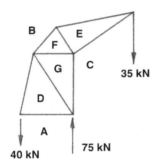

External forces acting on the truss are shown on the small diagram.

On the Maxwell diagram, the force values in red were those used to construct the diagram. All other force

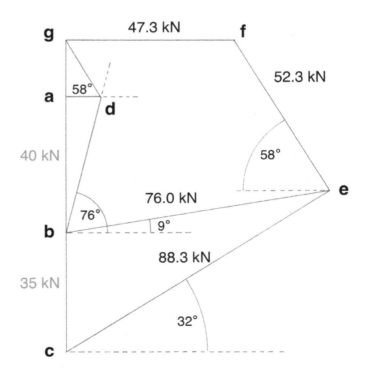

values have been read off the completed diagram, to scale.

From inspection of the completed Maxwell diagram:

Maximum compression

= 88.3 kN in the member between spaces C and E, and

maximum tension

= 76 kN in the member between spaces B and E.

151

Question 6

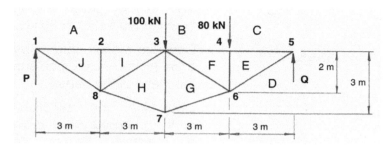

A pin-jointed bridge span carries two point loads, as shown. Ignore the weight of the bridge span, and determine the value of the reactions at the supports.

Then draw a Maxwell diagram to scale, using Bow's notation, to determine the forces in the respective members.

Solution:

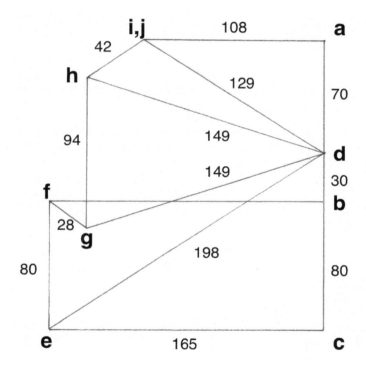

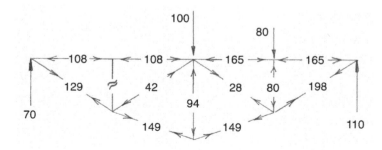

Analysing simple 3-D trusses: the Proportional Technique

For a three-dimensional structure to be considered a truss, the way that the members are joined at the nodes must allow rotation between members, in the same way that this was a stipulation in the case of 2-D trusses.

This criterion is fulfilled if solid members are joined by means of ball-and-socket joints. Ties in the structure that are made of flexible members like wire rope or chain cannot transmit rotation anyway.

Certain simple 3-D arrangements of struts and ties can easily be solved by methods similar to those used with 2-D trusses. However, 3-D arrangements carry an additional complication, as follows:

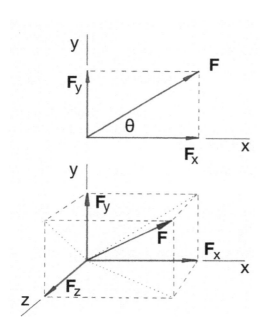

When we dealt with forces in one plane only, we had enough information to determine the relative magnitudes of the rectangular components of each force. Any force F had two components:

$$F_x = F \cos \theta; \qquad F_y = F \sin \theta$$

and the direction of the force F was defined by one angle, θ, specified relative to the x-axis.

However, when working in *three* dimensions, each force has *three* components: F_x, F_y and F_z. The direction of a force cannot be defined by one angle alone, but has to be defined by *three* angles.

This can make solutions that rely on calculations very complicated.

Also, when working with a 3-D structure, it is virtually impossible to conceive of a graphical solution that can be done on paper, because working in the plane of the paper is restricted to 2-D.

However, there is a method that simplifies calculations by dispensing with the need to specify angles.

This method, called the proportional technique, was developed by the present author, and relies on the fact that the tension in a tie *has to lie in the same direction* as the tie, just as the compressive force in a strut must lie in the direction of the strut. This is exactly the same observation that was made by Maxwell, though now applied in three dimensions.

The method is based on there being a unique constant of proportionality between the magnitude of each individual force and the length of the member carrying that force. The constant of proportionality for a given member allows us to solve for the force in that member. We can determine the unique constant of proportionality for any one member, if the displacements of the remote end of that member are known.

An example in 2-D will serve to illustrate the proportional relationship between the direction of the force in a tie and the direction of the tie:

Consider a force **F** applied at point **o** by a rope **oa**. Here are shown the force and its rectangular components superimposed on a diagram showing the *displacement* of point **a** from point **o**:

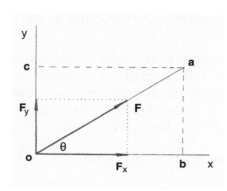

It is evident by similar triangles that the components of force F have the same proportions to one another as do the components of the displacements of point **a**.

By similar triangles: $F_x/(ob) = F_y/(oc) = F/(oa) = k$

$$\therefore F_x/(oa)_x = F_y/(oa)_y = F/(oa) = k \ldots\ldots\ldots\ldots(1)$$

Where k is the constant of proportionality relating the magnitude of the force in the rope to the length of the rope.

Each tie or strut in a given structure will have its own unique constant of proportionality.

In a 3-D situation, for a given member, the same constant of proportionality that applies in the x- and y- directions will apply in the z-direction, so that, similarly: $F_z/(oa)_z = k$

Visual proof of this statement is as follows: Here is shown (dotted line) a small rectangular space, one corner of which coincides with the origin of an x- y- z- system of orthogonal axes, and whose sides are parallel to those axes.

This small rectangular space is contained within a larger similar space, which, for the sake of example, has been drawn exactly three times the size of the smaller space.

It is readily observed that the line O a a' is a straight line.

It has to be so, since the two

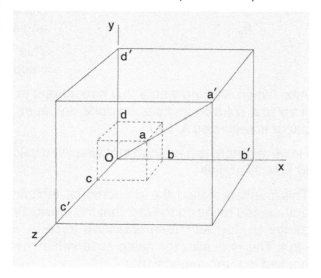

rectangular spaces are entirely proportional.

We have: $Oa/Oa' = Ob/Ob' = Oc/Oc' = Od/Od' = \frac{1}{3}$ (in this particular case)

Supposing we are interested in the force that a member Oa' is exerting at point O, and that the force in that member can be represented by the line Oa. Then the ratio of the magnitude of the force to the length of the member, namely the constant of proportionality, k, will be $\frac{1}{3}$ in this instance. If the larger rectangle had been four times the size of the smaller one, the value of k would be $\frac{1}{4}$.

If Oa represents the force F in the member, then Ob represents the x-component of that force, namely F_x; Oc represents F_z and Od represents F_y.

So, if we know the co-ordinates of the point where a tie or strut is fixed, at the end removed from the point whose equilibrium we need to consider, this gives us the three components of the displacement of that point. The three components of the *force* in that member, F_x, F_y and F_z, will be in proportion to the components of the *displacement* of that remote point.

Example

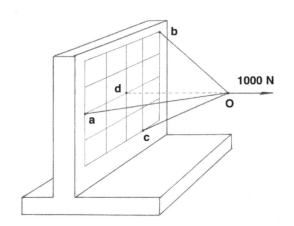

A horizontal load of 1000 N is applied to a rope as shown. This rope and three others converge at point 'O'. The other three ropes are respectively attached to points a, b and c on a flat vertical wall.

The grid drawn on the wall consists of squares 1 m × 1 m. The load rope is directly in line with point d. Distance Od = 3 m.

Determine the respective tensions in the ropes Oa, Ob, and Oc.

Method

Firstly, draw a set of orthogonal axes with its origin at point O. Show all the forces that converge at the origin. Label the force in rope Oa as 'A', and so on:

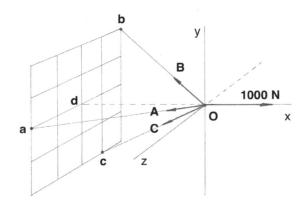

155

Secondly, determine the x, y and z-components of the *displacements* of points a, b and c from point O. These can be stated in metres or any other convenient unit of length, as long as they are all measured in the same units. The choice of units here is immaterial, as we are interested in proportions. We'll use metres in this example, as the data is given in metres. By inspection, from the diagram:

$(Oa)_x = -3$ $\qquad$ $(Oa)_y = 0$ $\qquad$ $(Oa)_z = 2$

$(Ob)_x = -3$ $\qquad$ $(Ob)_y = 2$ $\qquad$ $(Ob)_z = -2$

$(Oc)_x = -3$ $\qquad$ $(Oc)_y = -2$ $\qquad$ $(Oc)_z = -1$

Let the three unique constants of proportionality between each force and the displacement of the fixing point of the rope in which it occurs be k, l, and m respectively.

If we name the force in rope Oa as A, and the components of that force as A_x, A_y and A_z, then:

$A_x = k(Oa)_x$ $\quad$ $A_y = k(Oa)_y$ $\quad$ and $A_z = k(Oa)_z$, and likewise for the other two ropes:

$B_x = l(Ob)_x$ $\quad$ $B_y = l(Ob)_y$ $\quad$ and $B_z = l(Ob)_z$

$C_x = m(Oc)_x$ $\quad$ $C_y = m(Oc)_y$ $\quad$ and $C_z = m(Oc)_z$

Thirdly, we make use of the equations: $\Sigma F_x = 0$; $\Sigma F_y = 0$ and $\Sigma F_z = 0$ which apply, since the particle at point 'O' (at the junction of the ropes) is in equilibrium. Hence:

$\Sigma F_x = 0$ $\therefore$ $A_x + B_x + C_x + 1000 = 0$ $\therefore$ $k(-3) + l(-3) + m(-3) + 1000 = 0$ ....(1)

$\Sigma F_y = 0$ $\therefore$ $A_y + B_y + C_y = 0$ $\qquad$ $\therefore$ $k(0) + l(2) + m(-2) = 0$ ....(2)

$\Sigma F_z = 0$ $\therefore$ $A_z + B_z + C_z = 0$ $\qquad$ $\therefore$ $k(2) + l(-2) + m(-1) = 0$ ....(3)

Solving equations (1), (2) and (3) simultaneously yields:

k = 142.86; l = 95.238; and m = 95.238

Fourthly, we use the values of these constants of proportionality to determine the magnitude of the respective force components. In the case of force A:

$A_x = k(OA)_x = 142.86(-3) = -428.6$ N

$A_y = k(OA)_y = 142.86(0) = 0$

$A_z = k(OA)_z = 142.86(2) = 285.7$ N

Force A has magnitude $A = \sqrt{[A_x^2 + A_y^2 + A_z^2]} = \sqrt{[(-428.6)^2 + 0^2 + (285.7)^2]} = 515.1$ N

The reader may confirm, by a similar procedure applied to the components of forces B and C, that B = 392.7 N and C = 356.4 N

Exercises on forces in 3-D structures

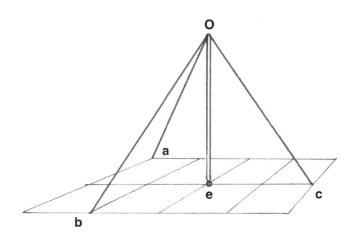

Question 1

A vertical pole, 4 m long, with a ball and socket joint at its lower end, is kept in equilibrium by three guy-ropes.

The grid shown on the concrete base consists of squares 1 m × 1 m. The tension in rope Oa is 10 kN. Determine the tensions in ropes Ob and Oc, and also the compressive force in the pole.

[Tension in Ob is 9.257 kN; in Oc is 14.64 kN and compression in the pole is 30.55 kN]

Question 2

A crane derrick stands on a concrete base, on which are shown squares 2 m on a side. The derrick consists of:

- A vertical pole **de**, attached to a horizontal concrete base by a ball and socket joint, braced with wire ropes to points **b** and **c**.

- A boom **ae**, which swivels freely, both horizontally and vertically, about the base of the upright pole at point **e**.

In the position shown the boom lies in a vertical plane 25° to one side of the centre-line of operation of the derrick.

A load of 10 kN is suspended from point **a**.

Determine the tensions in the ropes **ad**, **bd** and **cd**, and the compression in the vertical pole.

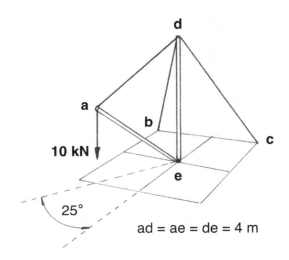

157

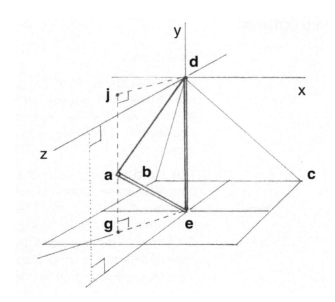

Hint: this diagram may help to determine the co-ordinates of point **a** with respect to the origin.

Some of the dimensions that are needed can be obtained by inspecting the plane **d-e-g-a-j**.

Answers:

Tensions in

ad = 10 kN;

bd = 6.124 kN;

cd = 15.09 kN, and compression

in the vertical pole = 12.32 kN

Question 3

Three rigid poles, O**a**, O**b** and O**c** are joined at point O by a joint that allows them to rotate freely relative to one another. The lower ends of these poles rest on a concrete base (assumed frictionless), and are held in place relative to one another by three wire ropes, **ab**, **bc** and **ca**. The grid shown on the base consists of squares of side 2 m. If a vertical load of 20 kN is applied to point O, determine:

- The upward ground reactions at the pole bases at **a**, **b** and **c** respectively.

- The respective compression values in all three poles, and

- The respective tensions in all three ropes.

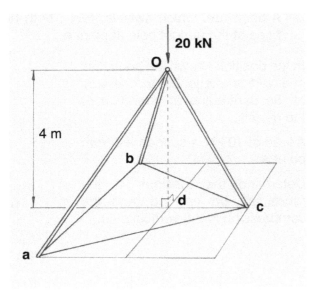

Answers:

Upward ground reactions at **a**: 5.0 kN; at **b**: 5.0 kN and at **c**: 10.0 kN

Compression force in the poles: in O**a**: 6.124 kN; in O**b**: 6.124 kN and in O**c**: 11.18 kN

Tensions in ropes: **ab** = 1.25 kN, **bc** = 2.796 kN and **ca** = 2.796 kN.

Practical projects to make and test pin-jointed trusses

Here are several ideas for students to put into practice what they have learnt about pin-jointed trusses. All involve building a bridge-like structure of manageable dimensions, out of relatively cheap, specified materials, and testing these structures to destruction, to compare their performances.

Naturally, two-dimensional trusses are inclined to warp when subjected to loading, so all structures for such projects should be effectively two similar trusses side-by-side, with the pins of the joints extending through both trusses, and the load applied to one or more pins between the two trusses.

Test equipment

If a compression-testing machine is available, a testing jig can be built to fit between the platform and the head of the compression piston.

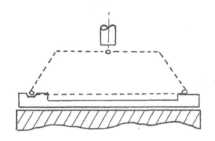

The size of the platform will usually restrict the length of the bridge to be built to approximately 600 mm.

Alternatively, a testing table can be built, with a built-in jig on which to place the truss that is going to be tested. When using the testing table, the load can be applied by adding mass-pieces to a load hanger suspended from selected pin-joints on the structure.

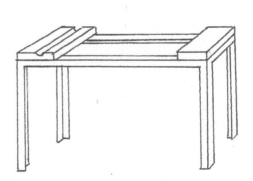
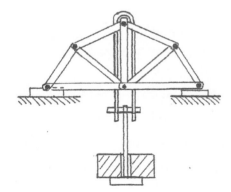

All participating students should be allowed to inspect the testing equipment before starting to design their bridges.

Dimensional and material specifications

Instructors need to communicate very clearly what the permissible dimensions of the envelope of the truss are, and where the load pin (or pins) and the support pins must be placed. The permissible range of width between the two sides of the structure must also be defined.

As long as a structure observes these dimensional specifications, fits into the test rig, uses only the specified materials, is properly pin-jointed throughout, and allows the load to be applied in the manner intended, the structure is acceptable. Non-compliant trusses are disqualified.

Materials must be clearly specified, and they must be the same for all participants. For example, one possible specification could be: 'All web members must be of 3 mm thick masonite strips, maximum width 25 mm, of any length, with 8 mm wooden dowels for pins'.

Students should be encouraged to test samples of the allocated materials to discover their limitations in tension and compression, before commencing to design their bridges.

Project type 1: Bridge with optimal strength-to-weight ratio

The purpose of this exercise is to obtain the best performance index (P.I.), where

P.I. = (load at failure) ÷ (weight of bridge)

Bridges are weighed immediately before being tested to destruction. Suggested scoring: the team with the highest P.I. scores 100% for the project. All other teams score in proportion, namely: Team score percentage = (team's P.I.) ÷ (best P.I.) × 100%

Project type 2: 'Planned sabotage' bridge construction

The bridge must be *designed to fail* within a specified range of load values. For example, the bridge must *not* fail while carrying a load of 10 kg, but *has to fail* before the load reaches 15 kg.

The team that built the bridge has to predict which of the bridge elements will fail first, and state this prediction in writing, to be handed to the instructor before the testing occurs.

Projects that comply with the specifications could earn partial marks as follows:

Surviving the lower limit: 40%   Failing before the upper limit: 30%

Correctly predicting which element will fail first: 30%

Project type 3: Strongest possible bridge construction

There is no limit on the number of web elements that may used, provided the mass of the bridge is below a specified maximum.The bridge must comply with all the requirements, especially in respect of being properly pin-jointed (no glue or any other fixing materials to be used) and must fit in the jig to be tested. For this project, the use of a compression testing machine is advised, as high load capacities can be expected.

The single performance criterion would be the load at failure. All teams score in proportion to the highest load at failure achieved by any team.

Alternative Test Apparatus

If a compression testing machine is not available, and the load has to be applied by adding mass-pieces to a load hanger, a lever can be used to multiply the loading effect of the suspended mass-pieces, as indicated in the following diagram:

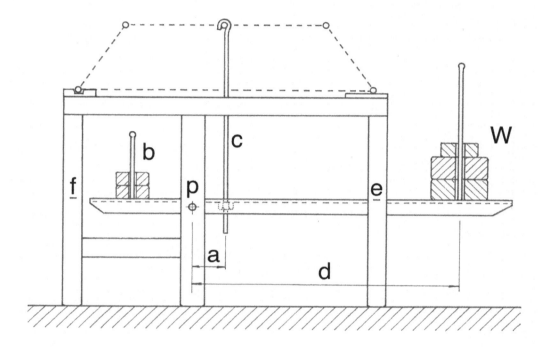

The lever is made from channel section, pivoted at point **p**, and must be balanced by adding weights at **b** until horizontal, indicated by levelling marks at **e** and **f**.

With the truss in place, and the lever balanced, the load application rod **c** is adjusted by turning a nut on its threaded lower end until the nut runs up to the underside of the channel. Now weights **W** can be added, starting at zero, until the truss fails.

Actual load on the structure of the bridge: **L = d/a(W)**

True/false questions to test your understanding of pin-jointed trusses and frames

1. A truss and a frame have identical characteristics.

2. A member carrying no load can be left out of a truss, with no ill effects.

3. A structure is over-constrained if it cannot be analysed by applying the equations of static equilibrium.

4. No-load members can be identified by inspection of a diagram of a truss.

5. The method of deducing by inspection whether a member will be in tension or compression is called the method of sections.

6. The method of sections involves making an imaginary cut, sectioning a portion of a truss.

7. If three web members converge at a node, one of those three members will always be a no-load member.

8. A node is the position of a pin-joint in a truss.

9. The forces in the members of a frame cannot be analysed by applying the equations of static equilibrium.

10. Trusses would be turned into frames by fixing the position of the members relative to one another, so that they are not free to rotate.

11. The members of a truss will individually experience some bending if the outer envelope (chord) of the truss undergoes a minor change of shape due to the loading on it.

12. A Maxwell diagram enables one to determine the forces in all the members of a truss under a particular loading.

Chapter 8

Friction between dry flat surfaces

Definition and contributory causes of friction

The factors that affect the magnitude of a frictional resistance

The limiting friction force, F_{max}

How to establish a value for the coefficient of friction between two given surfaces

The effect of surface area on the frictional force between two surfaces

The practical use of the coefficient of friction

Friction losses

The angle of friction, ϕ

The angle of repose

Practical applications and design projects

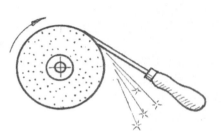

Definition and contributory causes of friction

What is friction, in a general sense?

In circumstances like the following, a natural resistance to motion is encountered:

1. Pulling a sled over sand

2. Stirring a thick liquid like syrup

3. Turning a wheel on a poorly lubricated axle

4. Rowing a boat on water

5. Throwing a table-tennis ball in air

6. Standing on a sloping plank while wearing rubber-soled shoes

The resistance to motion in all of these cases is caused by friction. Friction is the general name for the natural force which arises to resist an attempted motion.

Friction is not always undesirable. If it were not for friction, we could not walk, ride a bicycle, propel a car along a road, apply brakes, or rely on a nut and bolt to stay fastened. Shoelaces wouldn't stay tied. And, very significantly, early humans would not have been able to make fire. Without fire, there would have been no civilisation.

Although friction occurs in liquids (impeding the flow of water through a pipeline, for example) and in gases (as evidenced by the heat generated when meteorites enter the atmosphere), the present chapter focuses on the friction that occurs when one solid surface is slid over another solid surface, without lubrication, and without either surface becoming crushed to the point of breaking up.

Factors that contribute to the occurrence of friction

There are a few possible contributory causes of dry sliding friction, though they are not easy to isolate.

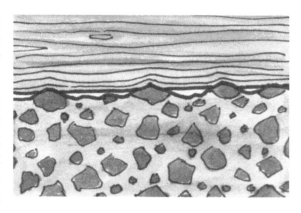

Consider a magnified section of two different surfaces in contact, being pushed against one another, while an attempt is made to slide one relative to the other. For example: wood on concrete.

The friction between these surfaces, or any others in contact, could be caused by any or all of the following:

1. The macro- and microscopic roughness of surfaces. The 'hills' of one surface interlock with the 'valleys' of the other. In order to get them sliding, minor deformations to these 'hills' may have to occur. This requires energy, and liberates heat.

2. Molecular attraction between the substances of the two surfaces, and

3. The flexibility of the softer of the two surfaces in contact, so that this material gets pushed into the 'valleys' of the harder material, and yields to the 'hills' of the harder material, thereby increasing the extent of the interlock between the two surfaces.

Factors like these collectively result in a resisting force that opposes the attempt to slide one surface over the other. It does not matter which combination of the three factors is actually responsible, because all of them could have an influence in resisting the sliding motion. What matters is that there is a single measurable effect, called the friction force.

It is important for engineers to know how to estimate the value of the friction force in different circumstances. If you know the magnitude of the friction force that is likely to arise, you can make use of friction to assist a mechanical design to function, or make provision to minimise any undesirable friction that occurs.

The factors that affect the magnitude of a frictional resistance

There are only two factors that affect the magnitude of the force needed to slide one un-lubricated surface over another:

- the amount of force pushing the two surfaces together, and
- the coefficient of friction for the combination of the two materials.

The force pushing two surfaces together

This is known as the normal reaction, **N**, because it is measured in a direction normal (perpendicular) to the two surfaces at their point of contact.

It has been found by experiment that the greater this normal reaction force, **N**, the greater the friction force at the interface.

Consider the following situations, and the free-body diagrams that apply to them: In each case the normal reaction, **N**, is determined by considering equilibrium in a direction perpendicular to the interface between the two objects in contact.

Below are shown four situations in which a block is in contact with a plane. Below each diagram is a free-body diagram of the block, from which the equation for the value of **N** is obtained. The weight of the block is W in each case. In the third and fourth diagrams, additional external forces have been introduced.

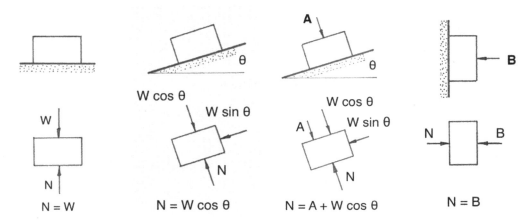

The coefficient of friction, μ

This coefficient, given the symbol μ (the Greek letter 'mu'), is a number, ranging in value from zero to approximately 1, that indicates the difficulty of sliding one material relative to the other.

The nature of the two materials in contact dictates what the coefficient of friction will be.

A coefficient of friction of zero indicates perfect 'smoothness', namely no frictional resistance whatsoever. A coefficient of friction of 1 indicates a large amount of frictional resistance. This value is sometimes regarded as the maximum possible value for μ. However, instances have been recorded in which $\mu > 1$. (See the table that follows.)

The friction coefficient has meaning only when *both* materials are specified. For example, 'the coefficient of friction for rubber on glass' can be specified. One cannot speak of the coefficient of friction for only one material, for example, for steel. If both surfaces are of the same material, for example: steel, then one must specify 'the coefficient of friction for steel on steel'.

It is important to realise that the terms 'smoothness' and 'roughness' that are sometimes used to indicate the extent of a frictional resistance, are not referring directly to the physical smoothness or roughness of the surfaces.

Some *very approximate* values for the coefficient of friction for various combinations are listed in the table below. These are averaged from various sources.

Value of μ	Combinations of materials exhibiting this value of μ
0.04	teflon on teflon
0.1	steel on teflon
0.2	nylon on nylon; hardwood on steel
0.3	leather on wood
0.4	wood on wood; brake material on cast iron
0.5	copper on steel; iron on iron
0.6	aluminium on steel
0.7	copper on glass; brick on brick
0.8	stone on stone (masonry)
0.9	zinc on cast iron
1.0	rubber on concrete; lead on steel
1.2	platinum on platinum

Despite the fact that some sources provide values of μ to two decimal places, the values for μ listed above have deliberately been specified to only *one* decimal place. (With the exception of the first item in the table.) This has been done because it is extremely difficult to establish a value for μ with greater accuracy than to one decimal place. Reasons for this difficulty are outlined further on in the present chapter.

The limiting friction force, F_{max}

To understand what the limiting friction force is, we have to consider what happens when we apply a force to slide one object relative to another. Suppose we attempt to push a heavy wooden crate along a floor.

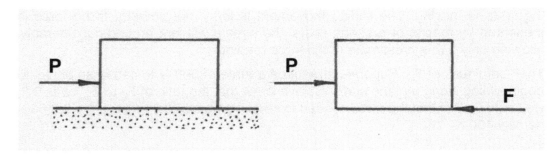

We apply a small force, **P**, that is initially *not* sufficient to slide the crate. We observe no movement. 'No movement' indicates equilibrium, so there must be a force that opposes **P**, and which is equal to **P**. This will be the friction force, which we can call **F**.

We continue to increase the value of **P**, gradually. As long as there is no movement, **F** must be equal to **P**. The reasoning for this is:

During the period of no movement, **F** cannot be less than **P**, as that would imply movement in the direction of **P**. Similarly, **F** cannot be greater than **P**, because that would mean that as soon as you try to push the crate to the right, the crate would move to the left, which is never observed in practice.

Thus, the friction force, **F**, will be equal to **P** while we gradually increase the magnitude of **P**, until, quite suddenly, the crate begins to move. Then we notice something interesting. Once the crate begins to move, the force needed to keep it moving drops slightly below its value at the point of movement, and remains waveringly steady after that.

A graph of **F** vs. **P** illustrates the above observations.

The maximum value reached by the friction force, **F**, just before movement occurs, is known as $F_{max.}$ The portion of the graph to the right of this point represents what happens if we should increase **P** beyond the value needed for motion to begin.

If we don't increase **P** beyond this value, the crate continues moving with constant velocity. If we do increase **P**, the crate will accelerate along the floor.

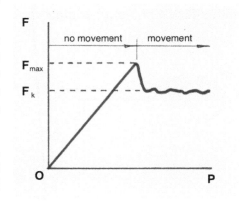

The kinetic friction force

While the crate is moving, whether or not it is accelerating, the friction force remains roughly at some level below F_{max}. This value of the friction force is known as the kinetic (meaning 'pertaining to movement') friction force, F_k. It is not easy to measure the kinetic friction force accurately, because one has to do this while the crate is moving. The sliding movement is jerky, not smooth. If the force is measured by means of a spring scale, the needle will jerk around considerably, allowing only a rough estimate of the force reading.

The usefulness of F_k : Suppose it requires a force of 500 N to cause an object to begin sliding along a plane surface. If we knew that the ratio of F_k to F_{max} was 0.8, we could predict that the force needed to *keep* the object sliding would be 0.8(500) namely 400 N.

The ratio of F_k to F_{max} varies for different combinations of surfaces. It can be as low as 14 % for some materials, or as high as 93% for others, according to various sources. The average value of this ratio (from 12 reported sets of values for different materials) is approximately 60%, which is a reasonable value to use for the purposes of speculative calculations. If you need a more accurate figure, you will have to determine it by performing an experiment using the specific materials that apply in your design.

How do we measure the magnitude of F_{max} ?

Apply a gradually increasing force **P** that attempts to slide one object over another, and note its maximum value, namely just on the point of movement. The maximum value of **P** is equal to F_{max} .

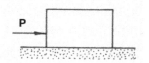

Determining the coefficient of friction between two given surfaces

Set up an apparatus as follows: One surface must be fixed horizontally. A block with a facing of the other material is placed on this surface.

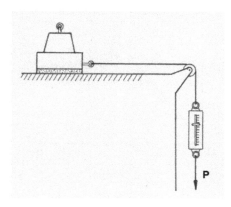

Start with the block at rest in a given (marked) position on the plane.Try to position this block in exactly the same place at the start of each reading, because the smallest variation in surface texture can affect the readings.

Vary the mass that is placed on the block. The normal reaction **N**, will equal the sum of the weight of the block and the mass that rests on it.

Pull the block with an ever-increasing force, **P**, until the block starts to move.

With a spring scale in-line, it is possible to keep a visual track of the force reading. With a free-running sheave arranged to guide the string, it is possible to ensure that the force on the block remains horizontal. This is important, because any vertical component of force in the string attached to the block will affect the value of **N**.

The following table shows results for a typical set of readings:

Normal reaction, **N** [N]	F_{max} (= **P** at point of movement) [N]
12	5.0
18	8.5
24	10.0
30	13.0
36	15.0

The following graph was plotted from results in the above table:

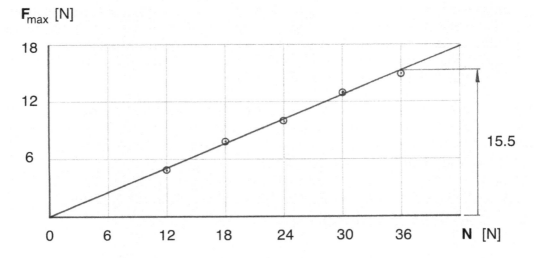

The graph shows that the magnitude of the limiting friction force is directly proportional to the normal reaction between the two surfaces. The graph can be represented by the equation $F_{max} = \mu N$, where μ = the gradient of the graph.

The graph ought to pass through the origin, since, if **N** = 0, there is no force pushing the two surfaces together, and so there can be no friction between them. Hence the co-ordinate (0; 0) must lie on the graph.

The gradient in this case is (a selected vertical dimension) ÷ (the corresponding horizontal dimension), namely (15.5 N) ÷ (36.0 N) = 0.4306 hence, μ = 0.43 for the two materials in this experiment.

It was mentioned earlier that it is very difficult to establish a value for μ that is accurate to more than one decimal place. The reasons for this have nothing to do with the reliability of the method used to obtain the value of the gradient. They have to do with the difficulty of getting repeatable results. Reasons:

- The frictional resistance varies slightly from place to place on a given machined surface, depending on minute variations in texture, and local patches of rust, dust, or oiliness.

- No machined surface is perfectly flat. And, if it were even close to being perfectly flat, then air would get excluded from the interface, with the result that external air pressure would be adding to the perceived normal reaction force, thus affecting the results.

- It is difficult to get exactly the same force reading when replicating a given set of observations during an experiment. This difficulty occurs because we have to judge the instant when the block begins to slide, and take the reading on the spring-scale virtually as the reading starts to change.

- Even though a source quoted in the literature may present results that depend on measurements performed with commendable thoroughness, if a source has indicated a result for materials of variable characteristics, such as 'wood on wood', or 'stone on stone', we cannot be sure if the same values would be found in an experiment done with just any wood, or any stone. Variations in type of wood, roughness of surface, and grain direction can make a significant difference to the experimentally determined value of μ.

For such reasons, unless you do an experiment to establish the value of μ for a pair of specific materials in the specific circumstances in which they will be used, there is little justification in accepting a value from the literature purporting to be accurate to more than one decimal place.

The effect of surface area on the frictional force between two surfaces

Does the amount of surface area in contact increase the frictional resistance? Most people would answer intuitively 'yes', assuming that if a small area offered a certain amount of resistance, then a larger area would offer more. Yet, this is not the case. It turns out that the amount of surface area in contact has no effect on the magnitude of the frictional resistance.

For example, suppose we placed a given weight on a wooden plank, and found that it required a force of 80 N to pull this plank across a horizontal surface.

If we cut the plank in half, and placed the cut-off piece of plank on top of the other to keep the total weight constant, we would find that the force required to cause the assembly to start moving was still 80 N.

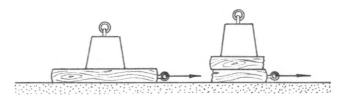

The easiest way of explaining this non-dependence on area is to consider the very sensible interpretation that the limiting friction force would be proportional to the pressure between the two surfaces as well as to the area in contact:

$F_{max} \propto$ (pressure) and $F_{max} \propto$ (area) $\therefore F_{max} = k$(pressure)(area) where k is some constant of proportionality.

However, pressure = (force) ÷ (area) $\therefore F_{max} = k$(force) = **μN**.

Hence F_{max} is independent of the area in contact. You can experiment with varying the area of two surfaces in contact, to verify this conclusion. At first this non-dependence on area seems counter-intuitive, but it is borne out in practice.

A popular misconception:

Enthusiasts often quote the fact that wider tyres give better grip on a road, as a reason why surface area 'must be a factor' in the magnitude of the friction force. It is true that wider tyres grip better, but they do so because they spread the heat released by friction over a larger area, thus reducing the likelihood that rubber will 'wipe' off the surface of the tyre. When rubber starts to wipe off a tyre, the tyre is melting on its surface, and can no longer sustain the frictional resistance that it is capable of when solid.

The practical use of the coefficient of friction

Knowing the value of the coefficient of friction for a given pair of surfaces enables us to determine the magnitude of the force needed to slide them relative to one another.

Example

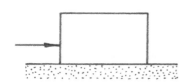

A block of concrete weighing 1000 N rests on a horizontal concrete slab. If the value of μ for concrete on concrete is 0.7, how much force is needed to make the block begin to slide?

The total force pushing the two surfaces together, N, is equal to the weight of the block in this instance.

There are no other forces perpendicular to the interface between the block and the slab.

Draw a free-body diagram for the block. Indicate the force P that is attempting to slide the block. The only force opposing P will be the friction force, F.

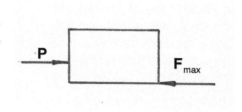

At the point of sliding, $P = F_{max}$. Also, $F_{max} = \mu N$. Therefore at the point of sliding,

$P = 0.7 \times 1000 = 700$ N.

Example

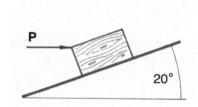

A wooden block weighing 400 N rests on a flat steel surface inclined at an angle of 20° to the horizontal. A horizontal force, P, is applied to the block, to make it slide up the plane.

The coefficient of friction between these two surfaces is 0.5. At what value of P will the block begin to slide?

Solution

Draw the free-body diagram of the block, with all forces reduced to components parallel to the plane and perpendicular to the plane. In this case, in addition to a component of the weight of the block, there is a component of force **P** that is assisting to push the block against the plane.

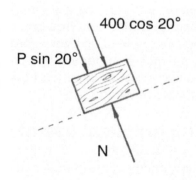

Consider all forces perpendicular to the plane: The normal reaction:

$N = 400 \cos 20° + P \sin 20°$..........(1)

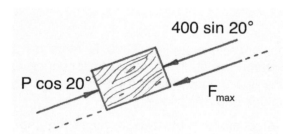

Consider all forces parallel to the plane: The attempted movement is up the plane, so the friction force will be directed down the plane. (Friction always opposes the attempted motion.)

Thus, at the point of sliding, $\mathbf{F}_{max}$ acts down the plane.

172

Also, at the point of sliding, the block is still in equilibrium, therefore the forces acting up the plane balance those acting down the plane.

Hence: P cos 20° = 400 sin 20° + F$_{max}$ ....(2)

But, F$_{max}$ = μN = μ(400 cos 20° + P sin 20°) ....from (1)

Substituting this expression for F$_{max}$ from (1) into (2):

P cos 20° = 400 sin 20° + 0.5(400 cos 20° + P sin 20°)

∴ P(cos 20° – 0.5 sin 20°) = 400 sin 20° + 0.5(400 cos 20°)

∴ when P = 422.5 N, the block will slide up the plane.

Friction exercises: set 1

In each of the following situations, the block weighs 100 N. Determine in each case:

1.   The magnitude of the normal reaction force, **N**,

2.   The direction and magnitude of **F**$_{max}$, and

3.   The magnitude of force **P** which will cause the block to slide.

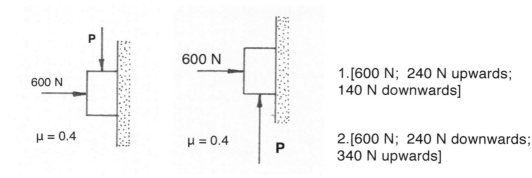

1.[600 N; 240 N upwards; 140 N downwards]

2.[600 N; 240 N downwards; 340 N upwards]

3. [20 N; 12 N to the left; 12 N to the right]

4. [146.6 N; 43.98 N downhill; 93.98 N uphill]

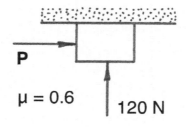

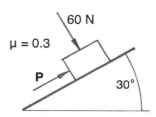

173

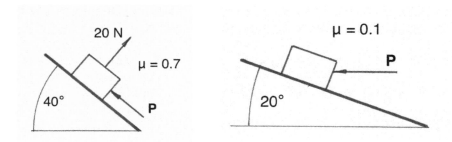

5. [56.6 N; 39.62 N downhill; 103.9 N uphill]

6. [110.4 N; 11.04 N down the plane; 48.15 N]

Determining whether or not a block will slide

Thus far, we have dealt with the straightforward question: *how much force* will get a block to slide? Now, we can go a step further, and consider *whether or not* a block will slide, given a particular set of forces acting on it.

The approach to questions of this type consists in assuming that the block slides one way, then analysing the forces to see if their resultant is consistent with sliding in that direction. If it is, the block slides.

If it isn't, one has to test the assumption that the block slides the opposite way, and check whether the balance of forces supports movement in that direction. If movement in both directions is impossible, the block will not slide.

Example

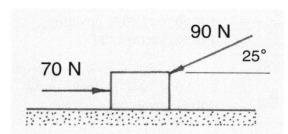

Consider a block weighing 100 N, resting on a horizontal plane where the coefficient of friction between the block and the plane is $\mu = 0.4$.

Two external forces, as shown, are applied to the block. Will the block slide, and if so, in which direction?

Solution:

1. Determine the value of the normal reaction:

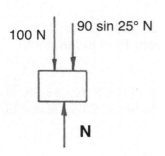

Firstly, draw a free-body diagram of the block. In this diagram the two downward forces, namely the weight of the block and the downward component of the 90 N force, are shown as parallel. Their exact lines of action are not important, as we are interested only in their effect on the block in the vertical direction. The block is clearly in equilibrium in the vertical direction, as there is

174

no reason for it to move up or down, given the forces acting on it.

Therefore, $\Sigma F_y = 0$ and thus:

N = 100 + 90 sin 25° = 138.04 N

2. If we suppose for the moment that the friction forces reaches its maximum value (*which it would only do if the block were on the point of sliding*) then $F_{max} = \mu N = 0.4(138.04) = 55.21$ N (*if attained*)

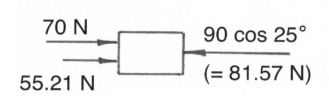

3. *Assume* that the block moves to the left, and check whether this assumption is justified.

If the block moves to the left, then F_{max} would be directed to oppose the motion, namely, to the right.

Sketch the force F_{max} acting to the right, and examine all the forces acting in the x-direction, along the horizontal plane.

It is evident that the sum of the forces to the right is greater than the sum of the forces to the left, ∴ the block can't move to the left, so our assumption that it did must be wrong.

4. Now test the assumption that the block moves *to the right*. If it does, then F_{max} must be directed to the left.

Show F_{max} acting to the left, and again examine all the forces acting in the x-direction.

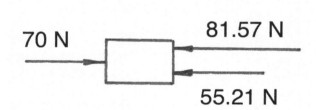

In this arrangement, the sum of the forces to the left exceeds the sum of the forces to the right, so the block cannot move to the right. Hence, our assumption that it did must be wrong.

5. Since we have shown that the block can move neither to the left, *nor* to the right, we conclude that under the action of the given forces, it *will not move*.

6. Since it does not move, we conclude that the friction force has *not* yet reached the value of F_{max}. This means that the friction force is only large enough to maintain equilibrium in the direction of *possible* sliding. The friction force acting on the block in this case would be: 90 cos 25° − 70 = 11.57 N to the right.

Example

A wooden plank weighs 256 N and is 4 m long. It is laid to lean against a wall, making an angle θ with the horizontal.

There is a frictionless roller at the end of the plank against the wall.

The coefficient of friction between the plank and the floor is 0.4.

If θ = 66°, will the plank slide?

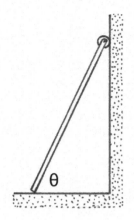

Solution

Draw a free-body diagram of the plank. Let the normal reaction at the floor be N_1.

Since there is a roller at the end in contact with the wall, the force that the wall can exert on the plank can only be horizontal. Let this force be N_2.

At the foot of the plank, there will be a friction force opposing the tendency to slide. Call this force F.

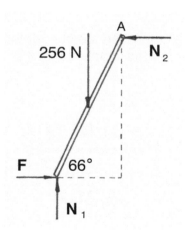

We have to test whether the value of F needed for equilibrium is greater than or equal to F_{max}. If it is, then the plank will slide. If it is not, the plank remains at rest.

Use any two of the the three conditions for equilibrium of the plank:

$\Sigma F_y = 0$ ∴ $N_1 = 256$ N. *If* the plank were to slide, the limiting friction force at the floor would be $F_{max} = \mu N_1$ = 0.4 × 256 N = 102.4 N.

$\Sigma M_A = 0$ ∴ 256 × 4 cos 66° = 256 × 2 cos 66° + F(4 sin 66°) ∴ F = 56.99 N.

This value < the value of F_{max} at the point of sliding, so the plank *will not* slide.

Friction exercises: set 2

Question 1

This block weighs 100 N. Will it slide? [yes]

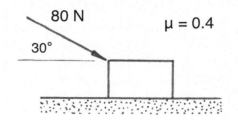

Question 2

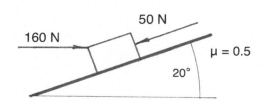

The block weighs 100 N. Determine the value of the normal reaction force between the block and the plane. [148.7 N]

Will the block slide? [no]

Question 3

The block weighs 200 N. Will it slide under its own weight? [yes]

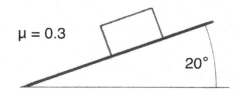

Question 4

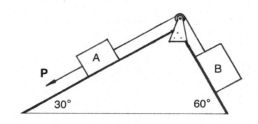

Two blocks are connected by a light cord passing over a frictionless sheave. Block 'A' weighs 50 N, and block 'B' weighs 100 N. μ = 0.5 on both planes. Determine the magnitude of force P that will just be sufficient to cause movement in the direction of P. [108.3 N]

If P = 0, will the system move or remain at rest? [move]

Question 5

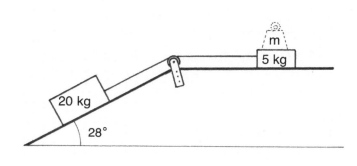

Two blocks, with masses respectively 20 and 5 kg, are connected by a light cord passing over a frictionless sheave.

The value of μ on the slope is 0.3 and that on the horizontal plane is 0.4.

A mass-piece 'm' is placed on the top block.

Determine the minimum value of 'm' that is sufficient to prevent the arrangement from sliding. [5.229 kg]

Question 6

The block weighs 100 N.

Determine the values of the normal reaction between the block and the ceiling, the limiting friction force F_{max}, and whether or not it slides.

$N = 60.98$ N

$F_{max} = 24.39$ N

Block slides to the left

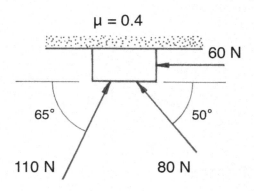

Friction Losses

In order to get two solid surfaces in contact to slide relative to one another, it is necessary to expend energy. Some of the energy thus expended results in movement, but a significant fraction of the energy becomes used up in creating minor surface deformations and vibrations, and in generating heat and sound.

Whereas the energy that results in movement may be put to good use, none of these other forms of energy is recoverable. The 'lost' energy is referred to as 'friction loss'. We can determine the magnitude of a friction loss by calculating how much work has had to be done against the friction force.

In a subsequent chapter on work, energy and power, in volume 2 of this series, there is more about the mechanical work done by a force, and work done against forces, including work done against friction. For the present, it is sufficient to know that friction on moving objects results in a loss of energy.

The Angle of Friction, φ (phi)

The angle of friction is a measure, similar to the coefficient of friction, describing how much friction exists between a pair of surfaces.

Using this measure instead of the coefficient of friction can greatly simplify the calculations in certain types of friction problems. The angle of friction is derived from the coefficient of friction, and is related to it as follows:

Consider the basic case of a single horizontal force, P, attempting to push a block of weight W along a horizontal plane, where the coefficient of friction is μ.

At the point of sliding, the friction force reaches its limiting value, F_{max}. There are four forces acting on the block:

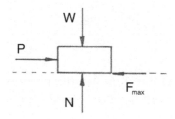

We can reduce these four forces to three, by deliberately combining two of them into a single resultant, R, and replacing these two forces with their resultant.

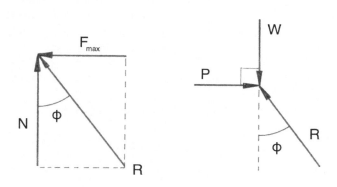

This is done by combining F_{max} with the normal reaction force, N.

The angle that R makes with the perpendicular to the two surfaces, is called φ, the angle of friction.

R therefore makes the angle φ with one of its components, the normal reaction force, N.

In the right-angled triangle in the diagram at left above, by inspection:

$F_{max}/N = \tan φ$, $\therefore μN/N = \tan φ$, $\therefore μ = \tan φ$

The greater the amount of friction, the greater is the coefficient of friction, and consequently, the greater is the angle of friction. Some typical values:

- If there is zero friction, $μ = 0$, and thus angle $φ = 0°$.
- For a low value of friction, say $μ = 0.2$, $\tan φ = 0.2$, therefore $φ = 11.3°$
- For a moderate value of friction, say $μ = 0.4$, $\tan φ = 0.4$, therefore $φ = 21.8°$
- When the friction is considerable, say $μ = 0.8$, $\tan φ = 0.8$, therefore $φ = 38.7°$
- If the coefficient of friction is very high, say $μ = 1$, then $φ = 45°$

Now that we have replaced F_{max} and N with their resultant, R, we have a situation where the block is in equilibrium under the action of only *three* forces.

These three forces can be represented by a triangle of forces, which can be solved to find the value of any unknown force.

The triangle must necessarily close, since the three forces

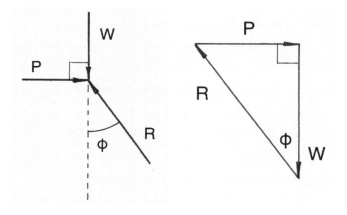

are in equilibrium at the moment when the block is about to slide.

Example

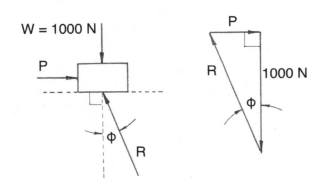

Determine the magnitude of the force P which will just cause a 1000 N block to slide on a horizontal plane where the coefficient of friction is 0.4.

We have $\phi = \tan^{-1}(0.4) = 21.8°$

From the triangle of forces,

$$P \div 1000 = \tan 21.8°$$

$$\therefore P = 400 \text{ N}$$

In the simple case used as the example above, the advantage of combining N and F_{max} into a single force, R, is not immediately apparent. However, in problems like the following, using the angle of friction simplifies the calculations significantly.

Example

Determine the magnitude of the horizontal force P which will just cause a block weighing 1000 N to slide up a plane angled at 20° to the horizontal, where the coefficient of friction is equal to 0.4.

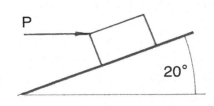

In cases like this, the unknown force P helps to push the block against the plane, thus contributing to the value of the normal reaction force. This means that there are components of an unknown force, in both the x- and y-directions, that will need to be taken into account.

To demonstrate the advantage of using the angle of friction, we will solve this problem firstly by the traditional method, and then using the angle of friction.

Method 1: Using the familiar equation: $F_{max} = \mu N$

Resolve all forces acting on the block into components parallel to the plane and perpendicular to it.

The normal reaction force N, is given by

$$N = 1000 \cos 20° + P \sin 20°$$

Now, $F_{max} = \mu N$

$$= 0.4 (1000 \cos 20° + P \sin 20°)........(1)$$

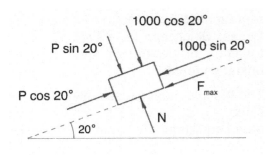

In the direction in which sliding might occur, at the point of sliding, there is equilibrium, so

$1000 \sin 20° - P \cos 20° + F_{max} = 0$ Substitute the value for F_{max} from (1) into this:

Therefore: $1000 \sin 20° - P \cos 20° + 0.4 (1000 \cos 20° + P \sin 20°) = 0$ ....(2)

$\therefore$ $342.020 - 0.93969 P + 375.877 + 0.136808 P = 0$

$\therefore$ $0.802882 P = 717.897$ $\therefore$ $P = 894.2$ N

Method 2: Using the angle of friction, ф

There are four forces acting on the block.

The first step is to reduce the four forces to three, by combining F_{max} and N into their resultant, R *(see diagram below)*.

The block is on the point of sliding *up* the plane, so F_{max} would act *down* the plane. This means that R lies *to the right* of the perpendicular line.

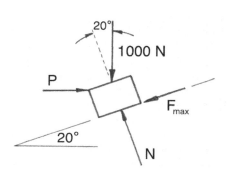

The free-body diagram we need to draw is simplified if we consider that there is no question of the block rotating. The equilibrium of the block may therefore be analysed as if it were a particle.

The first step in drawing the FBD is to draw construction lines showing respectively the plane, a perpendicular to the plane, and a vertical line passing through the point of intersection of the latter two lines.

Show the three forces acting on the 'particle'. Force R makes an angle of ф with the perpendicular line. This means that R makes an angle of (20° + ф) with a vertical line.

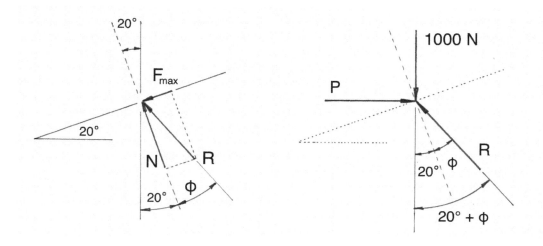

Now, we have three forces acting at a point. These three forces are in equilibrium. We can therefore draw a triangle of forces for these three forces, and the triangle has to close.

Since $\mu = 0.4$, $\phi = \tan^{-1}(0.4) = 21.8014°$

From the triangle of forces, we have

$P = 1000 \tan (20° + 21.8014°) = 894.2 \text{ N}$

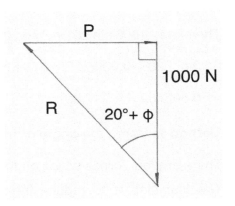

The calculations using this method were much simpler than those that were necessary when using the conventional method.

Now we look at a similar example, except this time the unknown force *reduces* the normal reaction between block and plane.

Example

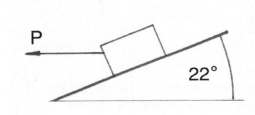

A block weighing 800 N rests on a plane angled at 22° to the horizontal. A horizontal force P is applied to the block. The coefficient of friction between the block and the plane is 0.6.

Determine the least value of force 'P' that will just get the bock to start sliding *down* the plane.

Draw the free-body diagram of the block showing the line of the plane, the normal line to the plane, and the perpendicular line at the point of contact. The normal line makes an angle of 22° with the vertical. Force 'R', the resultant of F_{max} and N, makes an angle of ϕ with the normal line. In this case, $\phi = \tan^{-1}(0.6) = 30.96°$.

A decision has to be made about which side of the normal line the force 'R' will lie. Since the attempted motion is to slide the block *down* the plane, the friction force must act *up* the plane, and therefore the force 'R' has a component directed *up* the plane.

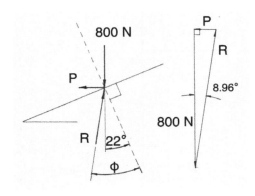

The diagram on the left shows the three forces acting on the block, and their respective directions. The diagram on the right shows the triangle of forces for the three forces acting on the block.

Solving the triangle of forces:

$P \div 800 = \tan (30.96° - 22°)$

$= \tan 8.96°$

$\therefore P = 126.2 \text{ N}$

182

Friction exercises, set 3: Angle of friction

Question 1

A block rests on a horizontal plane. A horizontal force, **P**, pushes on the block. Force **P** is increased slowly until the block begins to slide, which occurs when **P** reaches 168 N. If the angle of friction for this block on this plane is 32°, what is the mass of the block?   [27.41 kg]

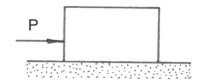

Question 2.

A wooden crate weighing 500 N is placed on a concrete ramp at an angle of 20° to the horizontal. The coefficient of friction is 0.8. Using the method of the angle of friction, determine the minimum value of the horizontal force needed to push the crate up the ramp.   [821.1 N]

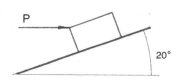

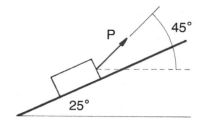

Question 3

An unknown horizontal force P acts on a block weighing 2000 N, resting on a plane that makes an angle of 35° with the horizontal. The coefficient of friction between the block and the plane is 0.3. Use the angle of friction to determine the magnitude of P that will:

Just cause the block to slide up the plane [2532 N], and

Just prevent the block from sliding down the plane [661.5 N].

Question 4

A plane with a steel surface is inclined at 25° to the horizontal. Resting on the plane is a copper block. An external force, P, angled at 45° to the horizontal attempts to pull the block up the plane. The coefficient of friction between these two surfaces is 0.5. The block begins to slide when P = 486 N. Use the angle of friction to determine the mass of the block. [62.83 kg]

The Angle of Repose

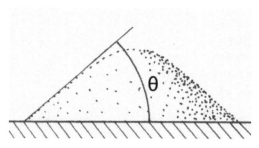

'Repose' means 'state of rest'. When dry sand is poured to make a heap, a particular type of sand always forms a heap with a particular angle to the horizontal. This angle at which the sand comes to rest, is called the angle of repose.

This particular resting position results because the sand particles keep rolling until they are in equilibrium.

If you try to make the heap steeper than the natural angle of repose, the sand rolls down until that angle is restored. The value of this angle depends on the amount of friction between the sand particles. The smoother and rounder they are, the smaller the angle of repose. In the extreme, think of trying to make a heap of marbles. The angle of repose would be zero.

To illustrate the angle of repose, place a brick on a wooden plank, and raise one end of the plank until the brick just begins to slide. The angle between the plank and the horizontal at the point of sliding is the angle of repose. If you placed a rubber mat on the plank, you could raise it to a greater angle before the brick would slide.

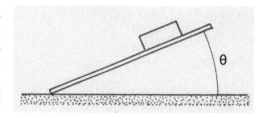

So, the angle of repose is clearly related to the amount of friction present.

It turns out that the angle of repose is identical with the angle of friction, ϕ.

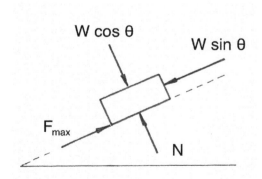

Proof: Consider a block, weight W, just on the point of sliding down a plane inclined at angle θ to the horizontal. At the point of sliding, the friction force reaches the value F_{max}.

Since the block is in equilibrium:

Perpendicular to the plane: $N = W \cos \theta$

Parallel to the plane: $F_{max} = W \sin\theta$

But, $F_{max} = \mu N$, $\therefore W \sin \theta = \mu(W \cos\theta)$ $\therefore \mu = (\sin \theta) \div (\cos \theta) = \tan \theta$

So, $\mu = \tan \theta$, but we have already seen that $\mu = \tan \phi$, therefore $\theta = \phi$

Note that this relationship is independent of the weight of the block.

If a block rests on a plane, the angle of the plane at which the block begins to slide under its own weight (namely, with no other forces acting on the block) is the angle of repose, which is equal to the angle of friction.

Example

A flat wooden board is raised at one end until a wooden block just begins to slide down it. At this point, the board is at 25° to the horizontal. What is the coefficient of friction between the block and the board? **Solution:** $\mu = \tan \theta$ ∴ $\mu = \tan 25° = 0.4663 \approx 0.47$, which is sufficiently precise an answer, on account of the difficulty of establishing a value for μ to more than one decimal place.

Example

An empty wooden box, mass 50 kg, just slides down a ramp angled at 30° to the horizontal. Determine the coefficient of friction between this box and this ramp.

Also determine the angle to which the ramp would need to be raised for the box to slide if a 100kg mass was placed inside the box.

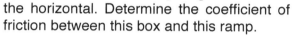

Solution: $\mu = \tan \theta = \tan \phi$ ∴ $\mu = \tan 30° = 0.58$

The angle of the ramp at which the box would begin to slide would not change, as the angle of repose is independent of the weight of the sliding object.

Friction exercises, set 4: Angle of repose

Question 1

A truck has a steel load-bed, which can be tilted for offloading. When a steel plate is placed on the load-bed, and the angle of the load-bed is increased gradually, it is found that the plate slides at an angle of 17°. Determine the coefficient of friction between the plate and the load-bed. If this truck is travelling on a horizontal stretch of road, with a plate on the load-bed, and brakes sharply, decelerating at 1.2 m/s², will the plate slide forwards?

[0.31; No, since the inertial force of the decelerating plate < F_{max}]

Question 2

A stone block of weight 684 N, placed on a wide steel beam, begins to slide under its own weight when the beam is raised to an angle of 32° with the horizontal. What magnitude of horizontal force would be needed to push the block up the beam, when the beam makes an angle of 20° with the horizontal? [875.5 N]

Friction exercises set 5: mixed examples

Question 1

A wooden plank weighs 300 N and is 4 m long. It is laid to lean against a wall, making an angle θ with the horizontal. The coefficient of friction between the plank and the floor is 0.4, and that between the plank and the wall is 0.5

At what angle θ will the plank slide?   [45°]

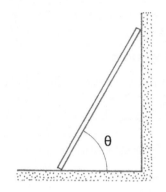

Question 2

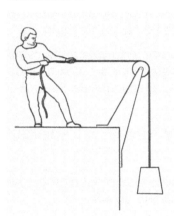

A man standing on a horizontal concrete roof holds a rope passing over a smooth-running sheave, connected to a load. If the man weighs 840 N and the coefficient of friction between his shoes and the rooftop is 0.7, what is the maximum load he can support at the other end of the rope?

If the kinetic friction coefficient is 80% of the static one, what would be the maximum safe load for him to support?   [588 N; 470 N]

Question 3

A block of stone with density 2500 kg/m^3 and dimensions 3 m × 2 m × 1 m has to be dragged up a stone ramp at 8° to the horizontal, by men pulling on ropes. If each man can exert a pull of 120 N parallel to the ramp, how many men will be needed? Use an appropriate μ value from the table given earlier in the chapter.   [1142 men]

If wooden rollers were placed under the stone block, reducing the effective value of μ to 0.05, how many men would be needed? [232 men]

This last exercise gives us an idea of some of the limitations of using manpower alone to raise such loads. How do you harness 232 men? If there are four rows of men, pulling side by side, each row needs to have about 60 men, one behind the other. If each row of men needed 1.6 m of space in which to pull, the column of men would take up about 100 m of ramp. That means the ramp would have to be built to extend 100m beyond the place where the stone needed to be offloaded.

If oxen were used instead of men, you would need fewer oxen, but each one would take up three times the length of ramp needed by a man. What does this say about the likelihood of the stone blocks of the pyramids having been dragged up temporary earthen ramps?

An interesting and quick experiment

In Question 3 above, a figure of 120 N was given, as the horizontal force that one man was assumed to be able to exert when pulling on a rope. You can verify the likelihood of this being a realistic figure. Attach a rope to a spring scale and the other end of the spring scale to a short rope attached to some fixed point on a wall. Pull on the rope as hard as you can, with your feet on the floor. Measure the force you can exert.

The friction between the soles of your shoes and the floor will be a major factor that limits the amount of force you can exert horizontally when pushing against a wall, or when pulling a horizontal rope attached to a wall, while your feet are only in contact with a level floor.

What will be the effect of having bare feet instead of shoes? What will be the effect of standing on a sloping ramp, and pulling uphill? What will be the effect of standing on sand? Use the information you glean from this experiment to tackle the following exercise:

Make an estimate of the coefficient of friction between a boat hull and beach sand, if it takes six men to pull a 220 kg rowing boat up a beach inclined at 10° to the horizontal. Assume they pull parallel to the beach.

Some practical applications of dry sliding friction

There are many applications in which our knowledge of friction is used as the basis of a design. Here follow just a few examples:

1. Cam cleats

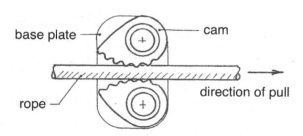

A cam cleat is a device which allows a rope to move through it in one direction, but not in the opposite direction.

Cam cleats are used in many applications, but most notably on sailing boats, where adjustments to the tension in the rigging have to be made quickly and reliably.

A cam cleat has a base that is attached to some fixed part of the structure of the boat.

On this base are mounted two sprung arms, placed at an angle θ to the line of the rope passing between their ends.

The rope can be pulled between the sprung arms, in the direction of the 'arrow' formed by the two arms. Any tension that tends to pull the rope in the opposite direction, causes the two arms to swing inwards, gripping the rope tightly.

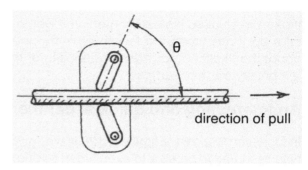

direction of pull

The greater the tension in the rope, the tighter is this grip.

Schematic diagram:

The angle of the two arms and the shapes of their ends are important, as they rely on friction with the rope to be pulled into a locking position. If angle θ is too small, the cleat won't work.

2. Mechanical clutches and brakes

Clutches are devices used to allow or discontinue the transmission of power from a rotating shaft to another shaft that has the same axis of rotation.

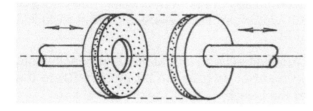

The essential feature of a friction clutch is shown here: two rotating surfaces that are engaged by means of an axial thrust pushing them together. The greater the thrust (namely, the normal reaction between the surfaces), the greater is the torque that can be transmitted. Clutches come in many different configurations.

A brake is a device used to slow down or prevent the rotary motion of machine parts. Mechanical brakes make use of friction to work against the rotation of a drum, shaft, wheel or disc. The four most common types of mechanical brake are illustrated below.

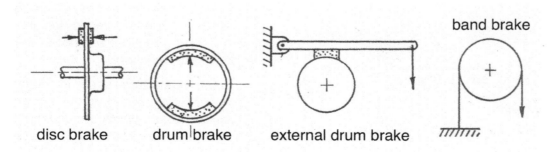

disc brake   drum brake   external drum brake   band brake

3. A pincer grab for lifting heavy slabs of stone, concrete or metal, that are positioned vertically.

A pincer grab is shown schematically here. The grab is suspended from a crane rope at A. The lower jaws (at D and E) are pulled open by an attendant and the pincer is lowered around the load. The crane rope is then raised.

The weight of the pincer mechanism by itself ensures that the upper arms that join the pincer to the crane rope are inclined to sag, causing nodes B and C to move closer together. This causes the jaws to close on the load as soon as the rope starts being raised.

The rubber-faced jaws grip the load, lightly at first. When the rope is raised, there is a downward friction force, F, exerted on the jaws by the load. This force contributes to closing the jaws even tighter. This can be seen on a free-body diagram of member BPE: the line of action of force F passes to the right of pivot P, thereby exerting a clockwise moment on the member.

The greater the tension in the rope, the tighter the grip of the jaws becomes. So the crane rope can be raised in complete confidence that the load won't slip. However, once the load has been settled on a supporting surface, the lower jaws are easily pulled apart by an attendant, thus freeing the load from the grab.

This type of crane grab is only suitable for lifting items that can withstand a significant amount of compression, because the normal force between the jaws can increase to multiples of the load value. It is advisable to have rubber facings on the jaws, as the arrangement relies on a high coefficient of friction to maintain the grip. The rubber facings also minimise local damage to the surface of the load.

A design-and-build project, making use of a knowledge of friction

A suitable topic for an engineering student design-and-build project, would be to make and test a pincer grab. Instructors would set the criteria for the performance index, the allowed materials, and the time-frame for completion of the project.

A performance index is a number allowing the functional merits of any two built designs to be compared. For example, if a pincer grab is to be made of specified

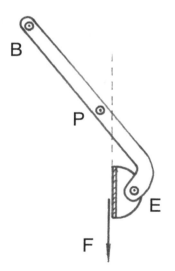

materials (say, hardboard, dowels and rubber sheet) then the performance index could be (mass of load raised before failure) ÷ (mass of pincer grab). Other conditions could apply, and those must be specified in the rules. For example, it could be specified that a minimum mass of 10kg needs to be raised, in order for a mark to be awarded.

Questions to test your understanding of friction

1. If you were wearing rubber-soled shoes, what would be the steepest angle of rock-face that you could walk up, without using ledges or handholds?

2. Consider the coefficient of friction between the skin on the bottom of your feet and a stone surface. Would this coefficient change if your feet were wet? How?

3. Does the equation $F_{max} = \mu N$ apply in all situations in which the magnitude of the friction force between two surfaces needs to be determined?

4. If one or both of two surfaces in contact is brittle enough to crumble from the pressure between them, would the effective coefficient of friction increase, decrease, or stay the same?

5. If a block rests on a plane where the coefficient of friction between the two is 0.4 and the angle of the plane is 25°, will the block slide?

6. In which situation does the use of the angle of friction simplify calculations: (a) where all the forces act parallel or perpendicularly to the plane, or (b) there are additional forces acting on the block, that are not parallel to the plane?

7. When we need to determine whether or not a given block will slide, under the action of a given set of forces, what assumptions do we need to make?

8. If you are pulling a load up a ramp by means of a rope, is there an optimum angle that you should maintain between the rope and the surface of the ramp? If so, why?

9. If you try to push a crate along a floor, by exerting a horizontal force by hand, does it matter how high up the crate you place your hands? Why?

10. If a horizontal force of 180 N attempts to push a crate that is resting on a floor, but the crate does not move, what does that tell us about the magnitude of the friction force between the crate and the floor?

11. For two given materials, can the value of μ_k (the coefficient of kinetic friction) ever be greater than the value of μ_s (the coefficient of static friction), and if so, in what circumstances?

12. For the simple situation of a block being pushed on a horizontal plane by a horizontal force, P, if a graph is plotted of friction force, F, vs. P, what value is shown by the gradient of this graph?

13. If you were determining the coefficient of friction for different wooden blocks on a given steel plane, would you expect μ to be higher for a soft wood or a hard wood? Why?

14. When performing an experiment to determine the coefficient of friction of a block on a plane, why is it important to start the block off in exactly the same position on the plane for each separate reading?

15. Should the graph of friction force, F, vs. normal reaction force, N, always pass through the origin? If so, why?

Chapter 9

Buoyancy

Definition and applications of buoyancy

The effect of the densities of the fluid and of the immersed object on flotation

The fraction of a floating object that will be submersed

Flotation of closed compartment and open vessels

How buoyancy affects submerged objects that are denser than the fluid

Artist's impression of the diving bell designed and built by Sir Edmond Halley (of comet fame) in 1790, for undersea work. The weighted barrel was filled with compressed air to replenish that used up by the divers. Illustration based upon contemporary engravings. The appearance of the diving suit and helmet are conjecture, based upon Halley's partial description, as no detailed drawing of them could be found.

Definition and applications of buoyancy

When an object is placed in a fluid (either a liquid or a gas) it experiences an upward force exerted on it by the fluid. This phenomenon is called buoyancy.

We have all had personal experience of buoyancy. You have seen boats and balls float on water, and have experienced feeling 'lighter' when standing in water than when standing in air. You also know that it takes a great deal of effort to submerge a beach ball or a soccer ball fully in water.

The first person to quantify the value of the buoyancy force was Archimedes, whose famous principle states that the buoyancy force on an object that is either immersed or floating, is equal to the weight of the fluid that has been displaced.

Archimedes' principle may be confirmed by a simple experiment.

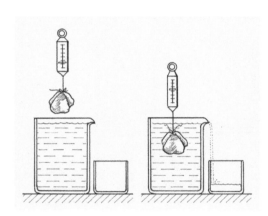

Suspend a heavy solid object, such as a stone, by a thin thread attached to a spring balance. Note the weight of the object, from the reading on the spring balance. While it is still attached to the thread, dip the object into a container of water that is full to the brim.

Now observe the reading on the spring balance, which indicates the (apparently diminished) weight of the object. Collect the displaced water, and weigh it. You will find that the amount by which the weight of the object appears to be reduced is equal to the weight of the displaced water.

Naturally, the actual weight of the suspended object does not change. The scale indicates a lower reading because the tension in the thread, force F, which previously equalled the weight of the stone, W, is now diminished by the value of the buoyancy force, B.

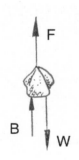

The phenomenon of buoyancy is observed in many engineering situations, and can be used to good effect in design.

Some applications of buoyancy

1. All boats, ships, and water craft of every description stay afloat due to buoyancy.

2. Hot air balloons, airships, and helium-filled balloons rise in air due to buoyancy.

3. Divers, diving bells and submarines experience buoyancy, and need to overcome the force of buoyancy if they are to remain below the surface.

4. Floats are sometimes used to control valves that need to open/close as a result of changes in the level of a liquid. Such floats are present in certain toilet cisterns, drinking troughs for stock on farms, and old-fashioned carburettors.

The effect of density on flotation

As a general principle, if the density of an object is less than that of the fluid in which it is placed, it will float. However, certain objects, such as ships, will float, even though they are made of material that is more dense than water. Before examining the details of what makes an object float, we need to become familiar with the densities of various commonly-encountered solids, liquids and gases.

The substance that we use as a standard for comparing the densities of all other substances, is fresh water. The density of fresh water is exactly 1000 kg/m^3 (that is, if one ignores very minor fluctuations due to temperature and pressure).

One litre of water has a mass of 1 kg. A cube which is 100 mm x 100 mm x 100 mm has volume 1 litre. There are 10 x 10 x 10 such cubes (namely 1000) in one cubic metre. Hence, the mass of one cubic metre of water is 1000 kg, or 1 tonne. For comparison, one cubic metre of steel would have a mass of 7.8 tonnes.

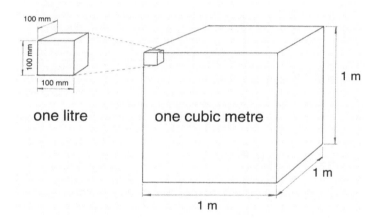

Three tables are provided below, listing the densities of some commonly-encountered liquids, gases and solids. The values in these tables have been obtained from various sources, which do not always agree closely.

Consider the given values to be average values, good enough in almost all situations for the purposes of realistic estimation in the examples and exercises that follow. If ever you need great accuracy for the value of a density, consult an authoritative source, or make the necessary measurements of weight and volume yourself.

In each of the three tables that follow, the densities are arranged from lowest to highest, for easy comparison. Density is allocated the symbol ρ (Greek letter rho).

Liquids, densities in kg/m³

These densities may vary with temperature and pressure. The values shown here apply at 0°C and one atmosphere of pressure.

Petrol	700	Sea water	1027
Ethyl alcohol	785	Water in the Dead Sea	1240
Motor oil	900	Honey	1420
Crude oil	900	Concentrated nitric acid	1560
Linseed oil	929	Concentrated sulphuric acid	1830
Fresh water	1000	Mercury	13590

Gases, densities in kg/m3

The densities of gases vary significantly with temperature and pressure. The values shown here apply at 0°C and one atmosphere of pressure.

Hydrogen	0.089
Helium	0.179
Nitrogen	1.251
Air (a mixture of gases)	1.290
Oxygen	1.429
Carbon Dioxide	1.997

Solids, densities in kg/m³

The densities of solids are subject to variation, too, although hardly any of this variation is due to pressure. Most of it is due to variations in the composition of the solids.

For instance:

- *The density of a metal alloy depends on the exact proportion of the constituents, which can vary from batch to batch.*

- *The density of wood varies, even from point to point within the same piece of wood, as growing conditions change during the growth of a tree.*

- *Timber grown in warmer climates is less dense than timber of the same species grown in cold climates.*

- *Lightweight concrete is made using chips of lighter material than the usual gravel, and the density can vary significantly, depending on which material has been used. Heavier concrete can be made by using iron ore aggregate instead of stone. This is sometimes done to coat underwater pipelines and stop them from being too buoyant.*

Expanded polystyrene	25	Quartz	2650
Polyurethane foam	30	Limestone	2700
Balsa wood	160	Granite	2700
Cork	240	Set cement	2800
Bamboo	350	Diamond	3500
Pine wood	500	Titanium	4500
Oak wood	750	Zinc	7134
Teak wood	800	Cast iron	7200
Lightweight concrete	800	Tin	7280
Ice (pure water ice)	917	Steel	7800
Raw rubber	950	Iron	7870
Processed rubber (soft)	1100	Brass	8400
Nylon	1150	Bronze	8800
Processed rubber (hard)	1200	Copper	8900
Ebony and Lignum Vitae	1200	Silver	10500
PVC (polyvinyl chloride)	1390	Lead	11300
Brick (fired clay)	1700	Tungsten	19300
Dense concrete	2300	Gold	19320
Glass	2600	Platinum	21450
Aluminium	2600	Iridium	22500

Although the average person is unlikely ever to see iridium, it is included in the table, as it is the densest naturally occurring substance on Earth.

To get a feeling for the magnitudes of these densities: compare the mass of one litre of each substance with that of one litre of water. From the table above, for example, one litre of expanded polystyrene would have a mass of 25 grams, one litre of concrete 2.3 kg, and one litre of gold 19.32 kg.

The ratio of the density of a substance to that of fresh water is known as the relative density of that substance. For example, from the table above, the relative density of granite is 2.7.

Rules for flotation of solid objects made from homogeneous material, placed in a fluid:

1. Objects less dense than the fluid will float in the fluid.
2. Objects whose density is equal to that of the fluid will be able to remain suspended at any depth within the fluid. Such objects are said to have neutral buoyancy.
3. Objects more dense than the fluid will sink in that fluid.

What fraction of a floating object will be submersed below the surface of the liquid?

A slab of expanded polystyrene will float in water with most of it sticking out of the water, while a block of oak wood will float with most of it below the surface. How do we establish the percentage of the volume of a homogeneous object that will stick out of the water?

In most of the examples that follow, we will be considering the flotation of objects in fresh water. However, the same principles apply to the calculations, irrespective of the nature of the fluid.

Consider a rectangular slab of material, with overall density ρ_o, floating in water, of density ρ_w.

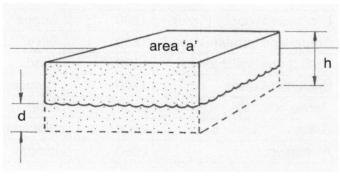

Let the surface area of the slab be 'a' and the height of the slab 'h'. The object floats with dimension 'd' submerged.

Since the object is floating, it will be displacing a weight of water that is *equal* to its own weight. The equation we need is derived from equating expressions for these two weights.

Firstly, the weight of water that is displaced = mg

= density of water × volume of displaced water × g $= \rho_w(a.d)g$

Secondly, the weight of the entire slab = density of slab × volume of slab × g $= \rho_o(a.h)g$

Equating these two weights, we have $\rho_w(a.d)g = \rho_o(a.h)g$ $\therefore d/h = \rho_o/\rho_w$, and thus:

The fraction of the volume of a floating object that is immersed is equal to the ratio between the two densities. If the liquid is water, this ratio is identical with the relative density of the object.

Examples

1. A slab of expanded polystyrene, of density 25 kg/m³, when placed on fresh water, will have 25/1000 of its volume submerged in the water. That is, 2.5% of the slab will be submerged.

2. An iceberg floating in sea water will have 917/1027 of its volume below the surface, namely 89.3%. Hence roughly 9/10 of it will be below the surface.

3. A block of oak wood floating in fresh water will have 750/1000 of its volume, or 75%, submerged.

4. A block of cork floating on the Dead Sea will have 240/1240, namely 19.4% of its volume submerged.

Exercises

1. Determine the percentage of the volume of a balsa wood log that will be submerged when the log floats in sea water. [15.6 %]

2. If a slab of aluminium is placed on the surface of a container of mercury, what fraction of the height of the slab will protrude from the surface of the mercury? [80.9 %]

Flotation of composite objects placed in a fluid

Flotation of closed-compartment objects

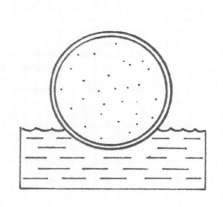

A closed-compartment object consists of a liquid-tight container enclosing other material, usually of lower density. Examples: all air-filled balls used in sport, sealed glass bottles, fishing floats, sealed oil drums, submarines.

The overall density of a composite object is defined as ρ_o = (total mass) ÷ (total volume)

A closed-compartment object will float, provided its overall density, ρ_o, is less than that of the liquid in which it is placed.

Example:

Determine the overall density of a beach ball made of PVC, outer diameter 300 mm and thickness 1 mm, containing pressurised air of density 2 kg/m³. Determine also the percentage of the volume of this ball that is submersed when floating in fresh water.

The volume of the PVC material (a hollow sphere) $v = (4/3)\pi (R^3 - r^3)$

$$= (4/3)\pi (0.15^3 - 0.149^3)$$

$$= 0.000281 \text{ m}^3$$

Mass of the PVC shell $= \rho v = 1390 \text{ kg/m}^3 (0.000281 \text{ m}^3) = 0.3904 \text{ kg}$

Volume of air inside the ball $= (4/3)\pi (0.149^3) = 0.013856 \text{ m}^3$

Mass of the air contained in the ball $= \rho v = 2(0.013856) = 0.0277 \text{ kg}$

Total mass of the ball $=$ mass of shell + mass of air $= 0.3904 + 0.0277 = 0.4181 \text{ kg}$

Total volume of ball $= (4/3)\pi (0.15^3) = 0.01413 \text{ m}^3$

Overall density of the ball, $\rho_o = m/v = 0.4181 \text{ kg} \div 0.01413 \text{ m}^3 = 29.59 \text{ kg/m}^3$

The fraction of the volume of this beach ball that will be submerged in the water when it floats will be $29.59 \text{ kg/m}^3 \div 1000 \text{ kg/m}^3$ or 2.959%.

Example

Will a full, sealed oil drum float in sea water? The mass of an empty thin-walled steel oil drum is 16 kg. Such a drum contains 200 litres of motor oil. The overall outer volume of the drum is 220 litres. Ignore the influence of the mass of the small amount of air inside the drum, and determine its overall density.

Mass of oil $= \rho v = 900 \text{ kg/m}^3 \times 0.2 \text{ m}^3 = 180 \text{ kg}$

Total mass $= 180 + 16 = 196 \text{ kg}$

Overall density of this composite object, $\rho_o = $ (total mass) $\div$ (total volume)

$= 196 \text{ kg} \div 0.22 \text{ m}^3 = 891 \text{ kg/m}^3$ Which is less than that of sea water, so the drum will float in the sea.

Flotation of open vessels

Open boats and other types of open vessels can be made to float in water, even if the density of the material from which they are made is greater than that of water. In order to float, an open vessel depends on having air in most of the space given up by the displaced water. When an open vessel floats, its

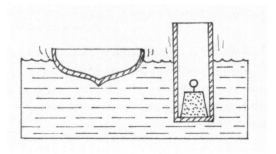

total mass is equal to the mass of the water it displaces.

Naturally, if an open structure such as a rowing boat is intended to float, it is important that it should be stable enough not to capsize. For stability, the shape of the vessel and the location of the centre of mass should be such that minor deviations from a desirable orientation should automatically be corrected. The conditions for the stability of such craft will not be discussed in detail in this chapter.

For the present, it is sufficient to know that when a boat or other open-structured vessel is floating, and tends to tilt slightly for any reason, the weight force and the buoyancy force are no longer vertically aligned.

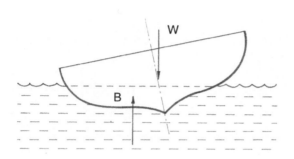

The weight force acts through the centre of mass of the boat, which ought not to change position unless load or people on board move laterally.

The buoyancy force acts through the centre of buoyancy, which coincides with the centre of mass of the volume of fluid that has been displaced.

If the moment produced by these two forces counteracts the tilt, the boat is stable.

If that moment assists in tilting the boat even further, the boat is unstable, and will capsize.

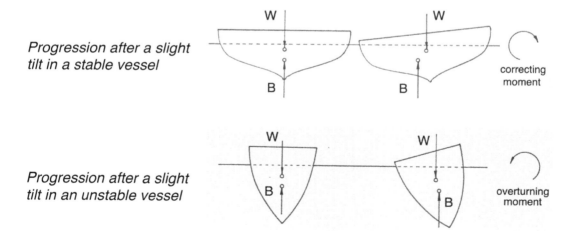

Progression after a slight tilt in a stable vessel

Progression after a slight tilt in an unstable vessel

Clearly, the shape of the submerged part of a vessel makes a big difference to its stability.

In the present chapter, however, we will not deal with the way that the centre of buoyancy of a vessel moves as the vessel tilts, but will confine ourselves to the discussion of the conditions required for floating, assuming the vessel remains stable.

Example

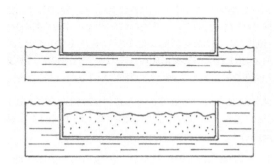

A square steel baking tray has dimensions 300 × 300 x 70 mm and mass 0.45 kg.

Determine the fraction of its height that will be immersed when the tray is empty and floating on fresh water; and the mass of sand that needs to be placed in the empty tray to get it to sink.

Let the tray be immersed to a depth d. Volume of displaced water = (d)(0.3 × 0.3)

Mass of the displaced water = ρv = 1000(d)(0.3 × 0.3) = 90 d

This mass must equal the mass of the tray, hence 90 d = 0.45 ∴ d = 0.005 m = 5 mm

Fraction of height immersed = 5 mm ÷ 70 mm = 0.07143 = 7.143 %

Mass of sand to be added to the empty tray to get it to sink: Let the amount of mass added be 'm'. Then, at the point when it is about to sink, the volume of water displaced must be equal to the volume of the container.

The volume of the container = 0.0063 m³, therefore the volume of the displaced water must also be 0.0063 m³.

Hence the mass of the displaced water is 1000 kg/m³ × 0.0063 m³ = 6.3 kg

Mass of container plus contents = mass of displaced water

∴ (0.45 + m) = 6.3 and hence m = 5.85 kg.

Example

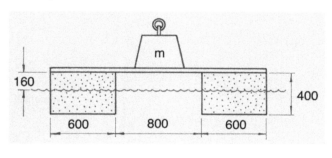

The mass of a composite wooden board, dimensions 2 m x 1 m, is 16 kg.

To this board are glued two identical slabs of expanded polystyrene that each have the dimensions 1000 × 600 × 400 mm.

a. How much mass, m, must be placed on the board when the assembly is floating in fresh water, so that the board is clear of the water by 160 mm?

The volume of the slabs is 2(1.0 × 0.6 × 0.4) = 0.48 m³

The mass of the slabs is given by $\rho v = 25 \times 0.48 = 12$ kg

If the slabs are to stick out of the water by 160 mm, then 240 mm of their height must be immersed. Volume of slabs that is immersed = $2(0.24 \times 1 \times 0.6) = 0.288$ m^3

$\therefore$ Mass of displaced water = $\rho v = 1000 \times 0.288 = 288$ kg

$\therefore$ Total mass of assembly must be 288 kg $\quad \therefore$ m + 16 + 12 = 288 $\quad \therefore$ m = 260 kg

b. What should be the value of m for the slabs to be just completely submersed?

The volume of displaced water would be the same as the total volume of the slabs, namely 0.48 m^3. Hence the mass of the displaced water = 480 kg

$\therefore$ m + 16 + 12 = 480 $\quad \therefore$ m = 452 kg

Exercises on buoyancy, set 1

Question 1 A 1000 mm long hollow cylindrical tube made of aluminium, with outer diameter 200 mm, has one end sealed. The mass of this tube is 3.52 kg.

Ten kilograms of sand is poured into the tube. The tube is then lowered into fresh water, and allowed to stabilise.

Determine dimension y, the length of the tube that will protrude from the water. [569.6 mm]

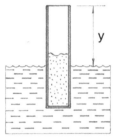

Question 2 A log of balsa wood is 6 m long and has average diameter 400 mm. How much downward force must be applied to this log, to immerse it completely in fresh water? [6213 N]

Question 3 A man of density 1010 kg/m^3 is swimming in fresh water. Someone throws him a ball of mass 1 kg and volume 11 litres, which he holds onto, for buoyancy. Is it physically possible for him to sink completely below the surface while holding onto the ball? [no]

Question 4 A five-litre oil can with mass 400 grams is emptied and then sealed, containing air. Determine:

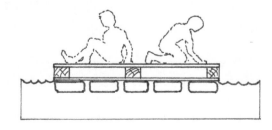

- The overall density of this can. [80 kg/m^3]

- The downward force needed to just submerge one such can. [45.13 N]

- Suppose that a number of such cans were fastened underneath a 20 kg wooden pallet to make a raft, which has to support two 70 kg people, without any part of the pallet becoming submerged. How many cans will be needed? [35 cans]

Question 5. An airship is to be filled with gas of density 0.2 kg/m^3, while the density of the surrounding air is 1.2 kg/m^3. *(Illustration shows Goodyear blimp of 1925, helium-filled.)*

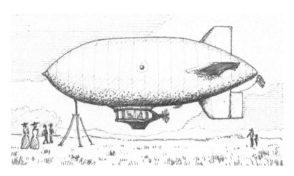

How much lift will be obtained for each cubic metre of gas contained in the airship? [9.81 N].The airship has to support its own weight as well as that of two 80 kg crew members. The mass of the cabin is 40 kg. The mass of the structure with its fabric skin works out at 0.5 kg for every cubic metre of the volume of gas contained. What should be the minimum volume of the gas in the airship?   [400 m^3]

Question 6.

A float in a tank consists of a hollow airtight cylinder constrained by a mechanism to move vertically. The cylinder has outside diameter 300 mm and height 1200 mm.

The balanced linkage transmits a force to bar PQ, which pushes down (via a roller) on a freely sliding piston supported by a coil spring, with force F.

When the water level in the tank is 200 mm above the bottom of the cylinder,

F = 0

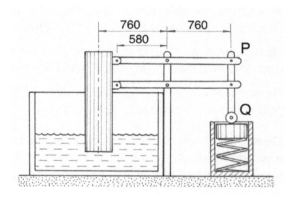

Determine the value of force F when the water level has risen to 500 mm above the bottom of the cylinder. [16.18 N]

How buoyancy affects submerged objects

Even if a solid object is too dense to float, it will experience a buoyancy force while immersed in a fluid. If it is supported by a rope, the tension in that rope will be diminished by the buoyancy force, so the apparent weight of the object will be less than its weight in air.

We will examine how the densities of the object and the fluid affect this apparent reduction in weight.

Consider an object suspended in water, with volume v and overall density ρ_o, where $\rho_o > \rho_w$

The buoyancy force, B, on this submerged object is equal to the weight of the displaced water.

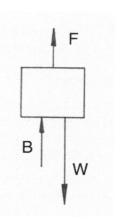

If the object is suspended from a rope anchored above the water surface, the force in this rope will be F, where , since $\Sigma F_y = 0$

$$F + B = W \qquad \therefore \ F = W - B \qquad \therefore \ F = (\rho_o v - \rho_w v)g$$

The ratio of the force in the rope (the apparent weight) to the weight of the object in air is given by F ÷ W,

namely $(\rho_o v - \rho_w v)g \div (\rho_o v)g = 1 - (\rho_w / \rho_o)$

Namely: 1 minus the ratio of the density of the fluid to the overall density of the submerged object.

For example, if a piece of ebony wood, ρ_o = 1200 kg/m³, is suspended in fresh water, the piece of wood will appear to weigh (1 – 1000/1200) as much as it does in air. This amounts to 0.1667, or 16.67 % of its weight in air.

Likewise, an object made of stone with a density of 2500 kg/m³, suspended in water, will appear to weigh (1 – 1000/2500) or 0.6 times its weight in air.

The table below shows the ratios of apparent weight in fresh water to weight in air, for some solid materials, based on similar calculations to the above:

Object made of	Density of this material, [kg/m³]	Ratio of object's weight in fresh water to its weight in air	Apparent mass of 1 cubic metre of this material [kg] when suspended in fresh water
Lignum Vitae (a heavy species of wood)	1200	0.1667	200
Brick	1700	0.4117	700
Concrete	2300	0.5652	1300
Stone	2500	0.6000	1500
Aluminium	2600	0.6154	1600
Cast Iron	7200	0.8611	6200
Steel	7800	0.8809	6800
Bronze	8800	0.8864	7800
Copper	8900	0.8876	7900

Two important conclusions can be made from the above table:

a. The apparent density of an immersed object is equal to its actual density minus the density of the fluid in which it is submerged, and

b. The more dense a substance is, *the less of a difference* immersion in a given fluid will make to its apparent weight when suspended in that fluid.

Example

A gold ingot weighs 400 N in air. If it were suspended in water, what would be the force reading on the spring balance? Ratio of weight in water to weight in air is 1 − (1000/19320) = 0.9482

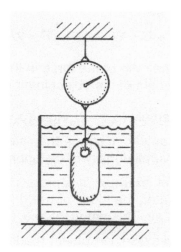

∴ reading on the scale will be 0.9482 × 400 = 379.3 N, which is not much of a reduction. By contrast, if it were suspended in mercury, the ratio would be 1 − (13590/19320) = 0.2966, and therefore the apparent weight would be 0.2966 × 400 N = 118.6 N, which does amount to a significant reduction.

Exercises on buoyancy, set 2

1. A lead sinker used in fishing registers 350 grams on a scale, in air. What would be its apparent mass when suspended in sea water? [319.0 grams]

2. A small cast-iron anchor being hauled out of a lake requires a force of 700 N to raise it. When it breaks the surface, how much force will be required to continue raising it? [812.9 N]

3. When raising an ancient bronze cannon from the ocean floor, while still immersed, the force in the rope is measured at 2150 N. The winch being used to raise the cannon is rated for a maximum load of 2400 N. Will it be safe to haul the cannon out of the water, using this winch? [No: the tension in the rope will be 2508 N, exceeding the winch's capacity.]

4. A small-boat sailor cruising among some islands has lost his stainless steel anchor of mass 45 kg. He decides to make a temporary anchor by enclosing some large stones in a net. Assuming the density of these stones is 2500 kg/m³, what mass of stone will be required? (Obviously the shape of the anchor is crucial to its function, but for the present, consider only the equivalent mass needed.) [66.33 kg]

General buoyancy exercises

Question 1

A thin concrete slab weighing 1400 N is used as a lid on a water tank. The fit is not air-tight. The tank is circular, with inside diameter 1.5 m. A block of expanded polystyrene with dimensions 1 m × 1 m × 0.5 m is placed on the water in the tank. Water is now added until the top of the polystyrene block just touches the underside of the concrete slab. How much more water needs to be added for the buoyancy of the block to start raising the slab?   [142.7 litres]

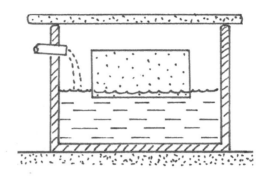

Question 2

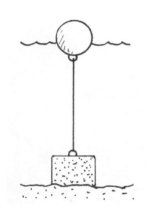

A spherical buoy of outer diameter 600 mm and mass 8 kg is tied to a concrete block of density 2300 kg/m³ and dimensions 600 × 600 × 400 mm.

Ignore the mass of the rope, and determine whether or not it will be possible for the buoyancy of this buoy to lift the concrete block off the ocean floor in high seas. [No: the maximum buoyancy force, when the sphere is totally immersed, is 1061 N, whereas the apparent weight of the concrete block in sea water is 1798 N.]

Determine the length of the side of a cube of concrete that would be the largest that this buoy could move when the buoy was completely immersed in a wave.   [440 mm]

Question 3

A diver with all his equipment has total mass 120 kg in air. This includes a weight belt sufficiently heavy to give him neutral buoyancy in sea water. If he discards 2 kg from his weight belt when underwater: a. What is the net upward force on him?   [19.46 N] b. With what acceleration will he ascend, assuming he makes no effort to assist or slow down his ascent? Ignore the resistance that the water offers to his progress.   [0.1649 m/s²]   c. How long will it take him to surface from a depth of 30 m?   [19 seconds]

Question 4

A flat rectangular plastic box which is airtight, floats on fresh water with 40 % of its height protruding from the surface of the water. What percentage would protrude if this box were placed in the Dead Sea?   [51.61%]

Question 5

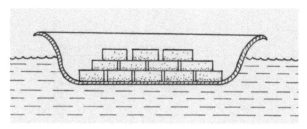

An empty cast-iron bathtub of mass 180 kg (assume rectangular in shape) is placed in a pond, and floats with 40% of its height sticking out of the water. What is the maximum number of bricks of average mass 3.2 kg that could be placed in this tub without sinking it?   [37]

Question 6

A steel machine part that weighs 72 N in air appears to weigh 64 N when suspended in oil, hanging from a thin thread. Determine the density of that oil.   [866.7 kg/m^3]

Tutorial Exercises on Buoyancy

The following exercises are suitable for tackling in groups.

Question 1

A house-boat on a lake is to have, as flotation, four sealed hollow aluminium cylinders, each 6 metres long, with outer diameter 600 mm. The walls of these cylinders are 3 mm thick.

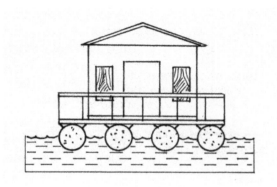

The cylinders are filled with expanded polystyrene to exclude water in case of a leak. The mass of the base frame that joins the four cylinders together and supports the house is 420 kg.

If the house, when devoid of occupants, is to float with all the cylinders half-submerged, what is the allowable mass of the house? [2077 kg]

If the house were built to this exact specification, how many people of average mass 80 kg would need to be in the house in order for the floats to be fully submerged? [28]

Question 2

An inventor wants to support a pedal-powered water craft on two cylindrical floats, each made of PVC pipe 3 mm thick, 3 metres long, with outside diameter 200 mm and additional hemispherical end-caps at both ends.

These floats are to be filled with polyurethane foam. The inventor wants the floats to be fully submerged, to reduce the surface tension drag.

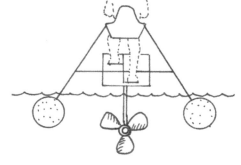

Determine the following:

The mass of the foam inside each float. [2.775 kg]

The mass of the PVC skin of each float. [8.251 kg]

The outer volume of both floats together. [0.1969 m³]

The mass of the craft (including the operator) that, when placed upon these floats, would just submerge them entirely. [174.8 kg]

Question 3

Refer to the illustration at the beginning of this chapter, showing the diving bell invented by Sir Edmond Halley.

a. How many 500 kg mass-pieces would be the *minimum* number sufficient to hold down such a diving bell, at the bottom of the ocean? Assume the following:

- The mass-pieces are made of cast iron,

- The volume of the interior of the bell is 37 m³,

- The bell is constructed of 2.5 m³ of oak wood and 0.5 m³ of wrought iron.

- Two occupants sit on the circular bench inside the bell. Each has a total mass of 100 kg, which includes their weight belts and equipment, and occupies a volume of 0.075m³.

Ignore any effects due to the increased pressure at the depth of operation (which is presumed not to be extreme). [answer: 8]

b. How would you get this diving bell into the water without it capsizing and losing its air?

For discussion and possible experimentation

Recall Galileo's experiment, when he dropped a heavy object and a lighter object together from the leaning tower of Pisa, and both objects hit the ground at the same time. Would this work out the same way in a medium considerably denser than air? Suppose you had two spheres, both the same size, one made of aluminium, and the other made of bronze. If you held them at the same level, just below the surface of the deep end of a swimming pool, and let go at the same time, would they hit the bottom together? Give your reasoning. What does this imply for the original experiment, conducted in air?

Index

About the Author

Gregory Pastoll PhD (Higher education, University of Cape Town, 1994) BSc Mechanical Engineering (University of the Witwatersrand, 1973) has had a 29-year career as an academic, shared equally between two fields, mechanical engineering instruction and teaching methods in higher education.

He has been a lecturer in mechanical engineering at The Cape Technikon, Cape Town, also at The Cape Peninsula University of Technology, Bellville, and senior lecturer in teaching methods at The University of Cape Town.

He taught basic engineering mechanics in a polytechnic/further education environment for over 14 years, being the subject co-ordinator of Mechanics 1 for some years and for Mechanics 2 for some years. He re-introduced lab experimentation into the teaching of mechanics in his department and started a tradition of using design-and-build projects for students to get hands-on experience of the principles they were supposed to be learning in class.

The author has also obtained teaching experience in two language academies, teaching English as a foreign language in South Korea (1 year) and Austria (2 years).

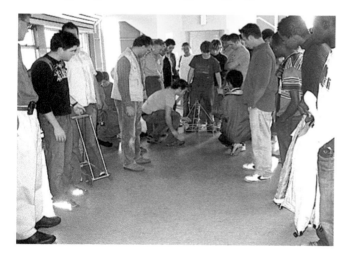

The author adjudicating student projects. In this case students had to design and build vehicles that had to travel as far as possible on a level floor, using a specified amount of energy supplied by a mass-piece descending through a height.

Photo by an unknown student, one of many assisting at projects such as these.

His other educational books are:

'Motivating People to Learn…and teachers to teach' (Authorhouse, 2009)

'Tutorials That Work' (Arrow Publishers, 1992).

The author has written and published fictional works, including children's stories, short stories in rhyme for adults, and the scripts for five musicals, two of which have been produced by a primary school. He has built three violins and designed and marketed a board game based on the sport of cricket. His hobbies are painting and woodwork.

Lightning Source UK Ltd.
Milton Keynes UK
UKHW051407101120
373137UK00003B/11

9 780648 466512